COGNITIVE SCIENCES AT THE LEADING EDGE

COGNITIVE SCIENCES AT THE LEADING EDGE

MIAO-KUN SUN
EDITOR

Nova Science Publishers, Inc.
New York

LIBRARY OF CONGRESS CATALOGING-IN-PUBLICATION DATA

Cognitive sciences at the leading edge / Miao-Kun Sun (editor).
    p. ; cm.
  Includes bibliographical references and index.
  ISBN 978-1-60456-051-0 (hardcover)
  1. Cognitive science. I. Sun, Miao-Kun.
  [DNLM: 1. Nerve Net--physiology. 2. Alzheimer Disease--physiopathology. 3. Cognition--physiology. 4. Models, Neurological. WL 102 C6765 2007]
  BF311.C5526 2007
  612.8'233--dc22
                        2007036193

Published by Nova Science Publishers, Inc. ✤ New York

CONTENTS

PREFACE

This new book focuses on new research on cognitive science which is most simply defined as the scientific study either of mind or of intelligence. It is an interdisciplinary study drawing from relevant fields including psychology, philosophy, neuroscience, linguistics, anthropology, computer science, biology, and physics. There are several approaches to the study of cognitive science. These approaches may be classified broadly as symbolic, connectionist, and dynamic systems. Symbolic - holds that cognition can be explained using operations on symbols, by means of explicit computational theories and models of mental (but not brain) processes analogous to the workings of a digital computer. Connectionist (subsymbolic) - holds that cognition can only be modeled and explained by using artificial neural networks on the level of physical brain properties. Hybrid systems - holds that cognition is best modeled using both connectionist and symbolic models, and possibly other computational techniques. Dynamic Systems - holds that cognition can be explained by means of a continuous dynamical system in which all the elements are interrelated, like the Watt Governor. The essential questions of cognitive science seem to be: What is intelligence? and How is it possible to model it computationally?

Chapter 1 – A memory undergoes a consolidation process in order to become stable. This new memory is de-stabilized when it is subsequently retrieved, but may undergo a reconsolidation phase, which allows the memory to be maintained. In recent years, memory reconsolidation has been the subject of much debate as well as excitement in the neuroscience community; not only because the phenomenon has extended the scope of the consolidation theory, but also because its discovery promises clinical applications, such as the treatment of post-traumatic stress disorders or drug addiction. Here the authors review recent advances in the study of the molecular processes underlying memory reconsolidation. Such studies aimed to provide mechanistic insights into memory reconsolidation, and to establish the relationship between memory consolidation and reconsolidation. The current findings lead to the hypothesis that memory reconsolidation is a partial recapitulation of memory consolidation.

Chapter 2 – Alzheimer's disease (AD) is a neurodegenerative disorder anatomically characterized by the appearance of neurofibrillary tangles and extracellular deposits of amyloid peptides ($A\beta$). Although the primary alteration is not established, accumulative data indicate that deposition of $A\beta$ in nerve terminals is the primary pathogenic event in this neurodegenerative process. Evidence indicates that glucose utilization is impaired in this disorder, suggesting that disruption of insulin and probably insulin-like growth factor I (IGF-I) signaling may be involved in the pathogenesis of AD. In this context, AD appears in the later periods of life when there is a progressive loss of sensitivity to IGF-I, as well as a decline in its circulating levels. In fact, decreased levels of IGF-I have been reported in familial forms of AD. However, high IGF-I and insulin levels are reported in the late onset form of this disease, reflecting a possible state of IGF-I resistance. Furthermore, animal models of familial AD suggest a disruption of IGF-I input that could be involved in Aβ accumulation. IGF-I is a physiologically important neurotrophic factor for both neurons and glial cells that is widely expressed in brain tissue early in development and, although reduced, this expression is maintained throughout adulthood. This growth factor possesses neurotrophic activities in areas severely affected in AD and its potential neuroprotective role could occur at least two levels. First, the activation of IGF-I receptors protects neurons against cell death induced by Aβ and IGF-I normalizes intracellular signaling pathways affected by Aβ. In this regard, IGF-I activates the phosphatidylinositol 3 kinase (PI3K)/Akt pathway, which is reduced in patients with a mutation of the Aβ precursor protein, and the Aβ induced increase in c-Jun kinase (JNK) is also blocked by IGF-I administration. In addition, given its capacity to modulate insulin actions, IGF-I may protect against the decrease in neuronal insulin sensitivity described in AD. Furthermore, IGF-I is reported to regulate brain Aβ levels by enhancing clearance of neurotoxic fragments, possibly by increasing the transport of Aβ carrier proteins such as albumin and transthyretin into the brain. Given that preliminary clinical trials show that treatment of insulin resistance in AD is beneficial and IGF-I infusion reduces brain Aβ deposits in mice over-expressing mutant Aβ, it follows that IGF-I could be a useful therapeutic agent for the treatment of AD.

Chapter 3 – Protein aggregation is the basis for many of the common human neurodegenerative diseases such as Alzheimer's disease (AD), Parkinson's disease and a family of disorders that includes Huntington's disease. In AD the aggregatory species is termed amyloid β (Aβ), a peptide derived from the proteolytic cleavage of amyloid precursor protein (APP), a ubiquitous transmembrane protein. The aggregatory properties of Aβ are determined by variations in the position of the proteolytic cleavage that generates the C-terminus. In healthy elderly individuals the ratio of the 40 amino acid peptide ($A\beta_{1-40}$) to the 42 amino acid species ($A\beta_{1-42}$) favours the less aggregatory $A\beta_{1-40}$ resulting in effective clearance of the peptide from the brain. In contrast, individuals who go on to develop the common sporadic form of AD have elevated $A\beta_{1-42}$ concentrations, or have a molar ratio of $A\beta_{1-40}$ to $A\beta_{1-42}$ that favours aggregation. In the five percent of AD cases that are inherited as an autosomal dominant trait all the causal mutations have been shown to favour Aβ aggregation, mostly by altering APP processing, either increasing $A\beta_{1-42}$ in absolute terms or in comparison to $A\beta_{1-40}$. In rare examples, where $A\beta_{1-42}$ levels are not elevated, mutations are found within the Aβ sequence that accelerate the intrinsic rate of peptide aggregation and stabilise particularly toxic subpopulations of aggregates, a clear example of this is the Arctic APP mutation.

In the context of cognitive decline, the demonstration of Aβ deposition in the brain in combination with intraneuronal aggregates of a microtubule-associated protein, tau, comprise the diagnostic criteria for AD. Mature deposits of Aβ are composed of ordered amyloid fibrils and it is their distinctive microscopic appearance and their affinity for dyes such as Congo red that favoured their early characterisation. However there is a poor correlation between the burden of amyloid plaques and the degree of cognitive impairment, indeed elderly individuals may have many plaques without showing signs of cognitive impairment. In contrast, it is the intracellular tau pathology that has been shown to correlate more closely with clinical deficits.

The location and progression of the tau lesions correlates well with the brain areas, such as the hippocampus, that are particularly impaired in AD.

The poor correlation between extracellular amyloid plaques and dementia has been used to detract from the significance of Aβ in the pathogenesis of AD. However recent evidence has clarified the situation, emphasising the toxic role of small Aβ aggregates rather than the amyloid fibrils. The finding that soluble Aβ correlates better with synaptic changes and cognitive deficits than plaque count has prompted the investigation of soluble aggregates of Aβ. These small aggregates can be purified by column chromatography and are composed of as few as 4 or as many as 180 Aβ molecules. When applied to cell cultures the oligomers are toxic whereas in most cases amyloid fibrils and Aβ monomers are not. When oligomers are visualised under electron or atomic force microscopes they are heterogeneous, including spheres, beads-on-a-string and doughnuts, but it seems that the spherical species are most toxic. Toxic oligomers may also be specifically detected, in vitro and in vivo, using rabbit antisera raised against Aβ immobilised on gold beads. The antiserum, described by Kayed and colleagues, binds specifically to small toxic aggregates of Aβ and neutralises their toxicity, in contrast the serum fails to detect monomeric or fibrillar forms of Aβ. Subsequent work has shown that the antiserum recognises an epitope on Aβ oligomers that is common to the oligomeric aggregates of a range of pathological proteins. The interesting corollary of this observation is that a common structural motif predicts a common mechanism of toxicity. This prediction is supported by work by Bucciantini et al. showing that oligomeric aggregates of a non disease related protein can elicit toxicity similar to that of Aβ oligomers in cell culture. Further work done in cell culture by Demuro and colleagues has shown that a shared ability to disturb membrane conductivity may underlie at least part of the toxicity of soluble protein aggregates.

However the hypothesis that soluble aggregates of Aβ represent a stable neurotoxic species has had to be reconsidered in the light of recent work showing that it is the ongoing process of aggregation that is toxic. It seems now that the soluble aggregates may simply be an efficient seed that can promote further addition of Aβ monomers. In their recent study, Wogulis and colleagues showed that, as expected, neither monomeric nor fibrillar Aβ were toxic to human or rat neuronal cell cultures. Their novel observation was that pre-treatment of cells with fibrillar Aβ, followed by a wash to remove unbound fibrils, primed the cells to die when they were subsequently treated with monomeric Aβ. The stability of the interaction of the fibrils with the cells was a surprise; following exposure to fibrils for only one hour the cells were still sensitized to the toxic effects of monomeric Aβ one week later.

With emphasis being placed on the oligomeric aggregates and the initial stages of the aggregation process, the mature plaques and tangles are increasingly being viewed as tombstones of pathological protein aggregation. Indeed there is evidence from cell-based models of Parkinson's disease that inclusions may be protective, reducing the rate of apoptosis [18] possibly by providing a sink for the disposal of toxic oligomers.

Chapter 4 – Disorder of consciousness is not an all-or-none phenomenon but it rather represents a continuum. Alzheimer's disease (AD) is the most common cause of dementia among people aged 65 and older, and patients are frequently unaware of the importance of their cognitive deficits (Derouesne et al., 1999). Vegetative state (VS) is a clinical entity with a complete lack of behavioural signs of awareness, but preserved arousal (ANA Committee on Ethical Affairs, 1993; The Multi-Society Task Force on PVS, 1994). Both clinical entities share a certain level of consciousness alteration, and a certain similarity in brain metabolic impairment. Here, the authors review differences and similarities in brain function between these two types of disorders of consciousness, as revealed by functional neuroimaging studies.

Chapter 5 – Communication is one of the fundamental components of both human and non-human animal behavior. Whereas the benefits of language in human evolution are obvious, other communication systems have also evolved to transmit information that is critical for survival. This review focuses on auditory communication signals, specifically species-specific vocalizations, and the underlying neural processes that may support their use in guiding goal-directed behavior. The authors first highlight the fundamental role that species-specific vocalizations play in the socioecology of several species of non-human primates, with a focus on rhesus monkeys (Macaca mulatta). Next, they review the structure and function of auditory cortical processing streams involved in spatial and non-spatial processing. Finally, they discuss the role that the ventrolateral prefrontal cortex may play in the categorization of species-specific vocalizations.

Chapter 6 – The endoplasmic reticulum (ER) plays an essential role in normal cell functioning and also in the pathogenesis of neuronal death. Irreparable perturbations in the homeostasis of the ER and alterations that lead to the accumulation of unfolded or misfolded protein in the ER lumen are thought to trigger several signalling pathways to restore the homeostasis of this organelle. These processes have been described to be involved in different important human diseases, including Alzheimer's disease (AD). Increasing evidences points to apoptosis as the major mechanism responsible for the neuronal death that occurs in this neurodegenerative disorder. In this context, mitochondrial dysfunction has been widely studied as a pathway integrated in the apoptosis that occurs in AD. It is an increasing assumption that the ER and the mitochondria cooperate in the mechanisms responsible for neuronal death and evidences suggest that mitochondria/ER crosstalk is also involved in AD. The recent and the novel research on ER stress and mitochondrial dysfunction and the cooperation between these two pathways can enhance the understanding of the molecular mechanisms that occur in AD and provide potential therapeutical targets.

Chapter 7 – The impact of the methodology of electroencephalography-based brain imaging on cognitive neuroscience has not been fully acknowledged yet. In particular, event-related brain potentials (ERPs) provide unique information to the study of the neural basis of human cognition. The article describes a Bayesian theory of the P300, perhaps the most studied ERP component. The theory was derived from several sources of knowledge. Firstly, empirical knowledge about factors that determine P300 amplitude and latency is considered. Here, the well recognized probability effect on the P300 proved to be the crucial factor. Secondly, Bayesian decision theory is shortly introduced. Recently, the conceptual framework of Bayesian statistics has been successfully applied to the sensorimotor system, and neuroscientific research on the Bayesian brain has just now been ignited. Thirdly, recent empirical knowledge about the neural basis of decision making is considered. A decision making model is shortly introduced because of its elegant simplicity, and due to the fact that it can be interpreted as a Bayesian decision maker. A Bayesian theory of the P300 arises from the integration of these different traces of knowledge, according to which P300 amplitude varies as function of Bayesian belief revision and P300 latency varies as a function of the duration of this revision process. The theory posits that the human brain codes and computes with probabilities, in a Bayesian manner, and that the P300 offers a window on the Bayesian brain.

Chapter 8 – The prefrontal cortex plays a central role in complex behaviors that require working memory, long term planning, appropriate response selection, etc. It has been known for some time that processing of emotional memories involves the medial prefrontal cortex (mPFC). Such emotional memories can be studied in animal models by using Pavlovian (classical) conditioning of autonomic adjustments. In the present review, papers reporting use of these techniques are first examined. It has now become apparent that, not only do learned autonomic responses involve mPFC control, but somatomotor Pavlovian conditioning also involves the mPFC. However, the conditions under which mPFC exerts control of somatomotor Pavlovian conditioning involve circumstances in which the conditions for acquisition of the response are not optimal, suggesting that prefrontal mechanisms are accessed only when higher level processing is required. Studies evaluating somatomotor conditioning, as a function of prefrontal involvement, are also reviewed, and a strategy for further understanding prefrontal control of these processes is outlined.

In: Cognitive Sciences at the Leading Edge
Editor: Miao-Kun Sun, pp. 1-8

ISBN: 978-1-60456-051-0
© 2008 Nova Science Publishers, Inc.

Chapter 1

MEMORY RECONSOLIDATION: A MOLECULAR PERSPECTIVE

*Laura S. J. von Hertzen and K. Peter Giese**

Wolfson Institute for Biomedical Research, University College London, Gower Street,
London, WC1E 6BT, UK

ABSTRACT

A memory undergoes a consolidation process in order to become stable. This new memory is de-stabilized when it is subsequently retrieved, but may undergo a reconsolidation phase, which allows the memory to be maintained. In recent years, memory reconsolidation has been the subject of much debate as well as excitement in the neuroscience community; not only because the phenomenon has extended the scope of the consolidation theory, but also because its discovery promises clinical applications, such as the treatment of post-traumatic stress disorders or drug addiction. Here we review recent advances in the study of the molecular processes underlying memory reconsolidation. Such studies aimed to provide mechanistic insights into memory reconsolidation, and to establish the relationship between memory consolidation and reconsolidation. The current findings lead to the hypothesis that memory reconsolidation is a partial recapitulation of memory consolidation.

INTRODUCTION

Fresh memories need to be stabilized in order to become long lasting through a process generally referred to as memory consolidation. Memory consolidation begins directly after training, and interference with the process impairs long-term but not short-term memory (for review, see Silva and Giese, 1994; Dudai, 2004). During memory consolidation de novo transcription and protein synthesis occur, and post-genomic studies suggest that a large

---

* Corresponding author: p.giese@ucl.ac.uk

number of proteins are synthesized (e.g., Levenson et al., 2004). It was long believed that memories undergo consolidation only once and that subsequently they remain permanent and unmodifiable. However, this so-called consolidation theory has been challenged by the finding that the retrieval of a consolidated memory can return the memory to a labile state, inducing a further consolidation process termed memory reconsolidation (Nader et al., 2000; Sara, 2000). During memory reconsolidation de novo transcription occurs (von Hertzen and Giese, 2005a), and inhibition of transcription or protein synthesis within a short time window after memory retrieval blocks memory reconsolidation, resulting in the loss of the previously consolidated memory (Nader et al., 2000; Taubenfeld et al., 2001; Anokhin et al., 2002; Debiec et al., 2002; Kida et al., 2002; Milekic and Alberini, 2002).

Much current research aims to understand the connection between memory consolidation and reconsolidation. One way of establishing this relationship is to undertake a molecular comparison of the two processes, because such a study can reveal whether memory reconsolidation is a recapitulation of memory consolidation, or whether the two processes actually differ. Understanding the nature of memory reconsolidation promises not only to advance the knowledge of long-term memory formation, but it also has potential clinical implications, including the development of physiopathological and therapeutic treatments for drug addiction and post-traumatic stress disorder using the concept of memory erasure.

COMPARING MOLECULAR PROCESSES UNDERLYING MEMORY CONSOLIDATION AND MEMORY RECONSOLIDATION

During memory consolidation and memory reconsolidation de novo transcription and protein synthesis occur. For the molecular comparison of the two processes one can apply various techniques to monitor changes in gene expression, such as real-time polymerase chain reaction or in situ hybridizations (e.g., von Hertzen and Giese, 2005a). For the analysis of gene expression during memory consolidation animals are trained in a memory task, and killed at different time points. Control groups (see below) are included in the analysis of gene expression to ensure that the expression changes are specific for memory consolidation. For the analysis of gene expression during memory reconsolidation animals are trained in a memory task, the memory is reactivated after memory consolidation is thought to be completed, and the animals are killed at different time points. Again control groups are used to ensure the expression changes are specific for memory reconsolidation. These gene expression studies reveal which molecular processes are engaged during memory consolidation and memory reconsolidation. Additionally, functional studies can be performed, which determine whether particular expression changes are essential for memory consolidation and/or memory reconsolidation.

A big confound in the comparative study of memory reconsolidation has been the use of behavioural tasks with different cognitive demands and anatomical substrates, which might explain inconsistencies observed in the field. Ideally, the mechanisms underlying memory consolidation and memory reconsolidation should be studied in single trial learning paradigms, as these tasks allow a clear temporal dissociation between the training phase and the memory consolidation phase, an advantage which cannot be exploited in multi-trial learning tasks. Fear conditioning, in which the animal learns to associate a neutral stimulus with a mild foot shock, has been frequently used in the study of memory reconsolidation (e.g., von Hertzen and Giese, 2005a). But other single trial learning tasks such as inhibitory avoidance (Taubenfeld et al., 2001), object recognition (Bozon et al., 2003), and odor discrimination have also been used (Tronel et al., 2002).

Another important factor to take into consideration is that memory consolidation and memory reconsolidation may engage distinct anatomical systems. For a particular behavioural task, one can properly compare memory consolidation and memory reconsolidation at the molecular level, if both processes involve the brain structure under investigation. For example, in studies of passive avoidance memory Alberini and colleagues showed that protein synthesis in the hippocampus is required for consolidation but not reconsolidation (Taubenfeld et al., 2001), whereas protein synthesis in the amygdala is required for reconsolidation but not consolidation (Tronel et al., 2005). Accordingly, the investigators showed that the transcription factor C/EBPβ is required in the hippocampus for consolidation but not reconsolidation of passive avoidance memory (Taubenfeld et al., 2001). It would be wrong to interpret these results as a demonstration that the hippocampus supports distinct molecular mechanisms for consolidation and reconsolidation of passive avoidance memory. Such a claim would be truly only possible if the hippocampus was required for both consolidation and reconsolidation in this behavioural paradigm. The hippocampus is essential for both the consolidation and reconsolidation of contextual fear memory (Debiec et al 2001). Therefore, the molecular differences between memory phases in the hippocampus are informative when the animals have been trained in contextual fear protocols (Lee et al., 2004; von Hertzen and Giese, 2005a).

Finally, the use of good experimental controls is also crucial. For example, the duration of the memory reactivation session determines whether or not it induces memory reconsolidation (Suzuki et al, 2004). When comparing molecular processes occurring after training to those observed after memory reactivation, one has to ensure that the memory reactivation triggers reconsolidation and not, for example, memory extinction, which would result in reduced task performance after memory reactivation (Suzuki et al, 2004). Furthermore, one must ensure that the changes observed are specific to memory consolidation or memory reconsolidation, and are not triggered, for example, by environmental factors alone. This can be accomplished by Pavlovian contextual fear conditioning, where one can neatly dissociate gene expression changes induced specifically by the conditioned stimulus (CS; context) or unconditioned stimulus (US; shock) from those induced by the CS-US association or memory reactivation (von Hertzen and Giese, 2005a). Such controls cannot be implemented for single trial learning tasks that use instinctive behaviour, such as novel object recognition. For such tasks as these, one cannot exclude the possibility that the gene expression changes observed after training are induced by the environment rather than by the initial learning.

DO MEMORY CONSOLIDATION AND MEMORY RECONSOLIDATION SHARE COMMON MECHANISMS?

To understand the nature of memory reconsolidation, recent studies have focused on molecular correlates of memory reconsolidation versus memory consolidation. An increasing number of such comparative studies have shown that the two phenomena share common molecular processes.

Comparisons of post-translational modifications occurring during memory consolidation and reconsolidation have shown that mitogen-activated protein kinase is phosphorylated in the hippocampus after both contextual fear conditioning and reactivation of the contextual fear memory (Kelly et al., 2003). Mitogen-activated protein kinase is also phosphorylated in the amydgala after both auditory fear conditioning and reactivation of the tone fear memory (Duvarci et al, 2005). Similar results have been reported for the transcription factor NF-KappaB, which is activated by phosphorylation in the hippocampus after both contextual fear conditioning and contextual fear memory reactivation (Merlo et al, 2005). However, these studies on post-translational events must be interpreted with caution; the modification of a protein by behavioural training need not be involved in the stabilising processes of memory consolidation and memory reconsolidation. Indeed, recently Chen and colleagues have shown that phosphorylation of phosphatidyinositol 3 kinase after contextual fear memory reactivation is required for memory retrieval, but not memory reconsolidation (Chen et al 2005). Thus, phosphorylation events after memory retrieval might not contribute to memory reconsolidation, though they might subserve quasi-instantaneous processes such as recall. It is open to question whether post-translational modifications are involved at all in stabilising memory.

In contrast, the relatively slow processes of memory consolidation and memory reconsolidation point to cellular events with slower kinetics, such as novel gene expression. Transcriptional analyses have shown that the genes encoding the serum/glucocorticoid kinase 1 (SGK-1) and 3 (SGK-3) as well as the transcription factors zif268 and c-fos are all upregulated in the hippocampus after contextual fear conditioning, as well as after re-exposure to the training context (Hall et al, 2000, 2001; Stanciu et al., 2000; Strekalova et al., 2003; von Hertzen and Giese, 2005a). The same carefully controlled experiments have shown, however, that three of these genes –SGK1, zif268 and c-fos– in addition to being regulated after conditioning and memory reactivation, are also regulated by the shock alone. As these genes may be fear and not memory regulated, they can therefore not be used to compare memory consolidation and reconsolidation; indeed, the upregulation observed after context–shock memory reactivation could be attributable to fear and not memory reactivation. Only genes that are specifically regulated by the learned CS-US association during consolidation are suitable for this molecular analysis. Interestingly, we have recently reported that during consolidation of contextual fear memory, SGK3 mRNA is upregulated specifically by the CS-US association, and that this up-regulation is recapitulated during contextual memory reconsolidation. As SGK-3 is not triggered by fear or other environmental factors during memory consolidation, the upregulation observed after re-exposure must be specific to memory reactivation. These data therefore show for the first time that memory consolidation and reconsolidation share at least some common processes at the transcriptional level (von Hertzen and Giese, 2005a).

Comparisons at the functional level have also shown similarities between memory consolidation and memory reconsolidation. Both the mitogen-activated protein kinase and the transcription factor zif268 are required for the consolidation and reconsolidation of recognition memory (Kelly et al. 2003, Bozon et al. 2003).

Thus, there is increasing evidence, both at the functional and molecular level, showing that memory consolidation and memory reconsolidation share at least some molecular processes.

ARE THERE MOLECULAR PROCESSES SPECIFIC TO MEMORY CONSOLIDATION OR MEMORY RECONSOLIDATION?

The increasing amount of data showing that memory consolidation and memory reconsolidation share common molecular processes suggests that the two phenomena are actually very similar in nature. However, this does not mean that they are identical. Indeed, while the evidence for common molecular mechanisms increases, so does that for distinctive features. Studies that have used contextual fear conditioning and analyzed molecular processes in the hippocampus, have revealed differences between memory consolidation and memory reconsolidation. Importantly, the hippocampus is required for both consolidation and reconsolidation of contextual fear memory (Debiec et al 2001) so that these molecular distinctions within the tissue are valid.

Two studies have provided evidence for the existence of memory consolidation-specific processes; processes that occur during memory consolidation but not reconsolidation. The hippocampal expression of the nerve growth factor inducible gene B (NGFI-B; also called nur77) is up-regulated during consolidation but not reconsolidation of contextual fear memory (von Hertzen and Giese, 2005a, b). Additionally, an antisense knock-down approach has shown that the brain-derived neurotrophic factor (BDNF) is required in the hippocampus for consolidation but not reconsolidation of contextual fear memory (Lee et al., 2004). Consistent with this finding, BDNF is up-regulated in an association-specific manner during consolidation of contextual fear memory (Hall et al., 2000). The up-regulation of both NGFI-B and BDNF during memory consolidation occurs predominantly in area CA1 of the hippocampus (Hall et al., 2000; von Hertzen and Giese, 2005a), thus area CA1 is likely to play an important role in consolidation-specific processes. Although BDNF expression has not been studied during reconsolidation, and thus it remains to be determined whether, as suggested by the antisense studies, the expression of BDNF is consolidation-specific, these two studies nonetheless provide convincing evidence that there are molecular processes specific to memory consolidation.

It has been argued that the occurrence of consolidation-specific processes is not surprising, and indeed should exist, because the animal experiences a CS-US pairing during training, whereas only the CS is presented during memory reactivation (Nader et al., 2005). However, these considerations neglect the fact that memory reactivation induces innate fear which is likely to be comparable to the fear triggered by the US. Thus, differences in gene expression observed between memory consolidation and reconsolidation are not at all reducible to differences in the external stimuli present. This idea is supported by our finding that the expression of the association-specific transcript SGK-3 is up-regulated during both the consolidation and reconsolidation of contextual fear memory (von Hertzen and Giese, 2005a). Since in principle all molecular processes could behave like the SGK-3 expression, the existence of molecular processes specific to memory consolidation shows that there is a mechanistic difference between memory consolidation and memory reconsolidation.

A recent antisense study has tended to confirm that in addition to consolidation-specific processes, reconsolidation-specific processes also exist. Knock-down of the transcription factor zif268 in the hippocampus was shown to block reconsolidation but not consolidation of contextual fear memory (Lee et al., 2004). This finding is nevertheless surprising because other functional studies have shown that zif268 is required for the consolidation of various forms of memory (Jones et al., 2000; Bozon et al., 2003; Malkani et al., 2004). Furthermore, zif268 expression is upregulated in the hippocampus during both consolidation and reconsolidation (Hall et al., 2000, 2001), and it is not clear whether the expression change during reconsolidation is specific to memory reactivation. A problem is that repeated exposure to the context without conditioning leads to an increase in hippocampal zif268 expression. Because this zif268 expression change is smaller than the expression change after reactivation of contextual fear memory it has been argued that there would be memory reconsolidation-specific zif268 expression. However, a latent inhibition control group showed that fear can up-regulate hippocampal zif268 expression. Thus, the innate fear during reactivation of contextual fear memory may have potentiated the increase in zif268 expression, and a memory reconsolidation-specific zif268 expression change might not exist. Therefore, it is at this stage premature to conclude that reconsolidation specific processes exist. However, Lee et al. nevertheless provide further evidence that there are differences between memory consolidation and memory reconsolidation.

MEMORY RECONSOLIDATION AS A PARTIAL RECAPITULATION OF MEMORY CONSOLIDATION

The data from comparative studies on the molecular mechanisms underlying memory consolidation and memory reconsolidation have led us to the hypothesis that reconsolidation is a partial recapitulation of consolidation (von Hertzen and Giese, 2005a). This hypothesis is based on the findings that I) memory consolidation and memory reconsolidation share common molecular processes, such as the up-regulation of SGK-3 expression, and II) memory consolidation-specific processes exist in addition. This theory therefore proposes that a larger number of molecular processes are engaged during memory consolidation than during memory reconsolidation. This would be consistent with the idea that establishing a new memory is likely to require more substantial alteration at the cellular level than maintaining an already existing memory. The reconsolidated memory might have a sparser representation that is actively maintained by fewer genes.

It is very likely that there is functional redundancy between some of the molecular processes occurring during memory formation, because microarray studies imply that some functionally related genes might be regulated in the same way. If this assumption is correct, then, according to our hypothesis, there would be less functional redundancy during memory reconsolidation than during memory consolidation. Such a difference in functional redundancy would explain why contextual memory reconsolidation but not consolidation is affected by a knock-down of zif268 in the hippocampus.

In conclusion, memory reconsolidation appears to be a partial recapitulation of consolidation, differing from consolidation merely in that it only engages a subset of the processes required for memory consolidation. Such partial rather than total recapitulation may have evolved as a more economic and reliable mechanism for an organism to maintain a memory.

ACKNOWLEDGEMENTS

We are grateful to Jeff Vernon for comments on an earlier draft of this manuscript. This work was supported by the Wellcome Trust.

REFERENCES

Anokhin, K.V., Tiunova, A.A., Rose, S.P. Reminder effects - reconsolidation or retrieval deficit? Pharmacological dissection with protein synthesis inhibitors following reminder for a passiveavoidance task in young chicks. *Eur. J. Neurosci.* 15: 1759-1765, 2002.

Bozon, B., Davis, S., Laroche, S. A requirement for the immediate early gene zif268 in reconsolidation of recognition memory after retrieval. *Neuron* 40: 695-701, 2003.

Chen, X., Garelick, M.G., Wang, H., Lil, V., Athos, J., Storm, D.R. PI3 kinase signaling is required for retrieval and extinction of contextual memory. *Nat. Neurosci.* 8: 925-931, 2005.

Debiec, J., LeDoux, J.E., Nader, K. Cellular and systems reconsolidation in the hippocampus. *Neuron* 36: 527-538, 2002.

Dudai, Y. The neurobiology of consolidations, or, how stable is the engram? *Annu. Rev. Psychol.* 55: 51-86, 2004.

Duvarci, S., Nader, K., LeDoux, J.E. Activation of extracellular signal-regulated kinase-mitogenactivated protein kinase cascade in the amygdala is required for memory reconsolidation of auditory fear conditioning. *Eur. J. Neurosci.* 21: 283-289, 2005.

Hall, J., Thomas, K.L., Everitt, B.J. Rapid and selective induction of BDNF expression in the hippocampus during contextual learning. *Nat. Neurosci.* 3: 533-535, 2000.

Hall, J., Thomas, K.L., Everitt, B.J. Cellular imaging of zif268 expression in the hippocampus and amygdala during contextual and cued fear memory retrieval: selective activation of hippocampal CA1 neurons during the recall of contextual memories. *J. Neurosci.* 21: 2186-2193, 2001.

Jones, M.W., Errington, M.L., French, P.J., Fine, A., Bliss, T.V.P., Garel, S., Charnay, P., Bozon, B., Laroche, S., Davis, S. A requirement for the immediate early gene zif268 in the expression of late LTP and long-term memories. *Nat. Neurosci.* 4: 289-296, 2001.

Kelly, A., Laroche, S., Davis, S. Activation of mitogen-activated protein kinase/extracellular signalregulated kinase in hippocampal circuitry is required for consolidation and reconsolidation of recognition memory. *J. Neurosci.* 23: 5354-5360, 2003.

Kida, S., Josselyn, S.A., de Ortiz, S.P., Kogan, J.H., Chevere, I., Masushige, S., Silva, A.J. CREB required for the stability of new and reactivated fear memories. *Nat. Neurosci.* 5: 348-355, 2002.

Lee, J.L., Everitt, B.J., Thomas, K.L. Independent cellular processes for hippocampal memory consolidation and reconsolidation. *Science* 304: 839-843, 2004.

Levenson, J.M., Choi, S., Lee, S.Y., Cao, Y.A., Ahn, H.J., Worley, K.C., Pizzi, M., Liou, H.C., Sweatt, J.D. A bioinformatics analysis of memory consolidation reveals involvement of the transcription factor c-rel. *J. Neurosci.* 24: 3933-3943, 2004.

Malkani, S., Wallace, K.J., Donley, M.P., Rosen, J.B. An egr-1 (zif268) antisense oligodeoxynucleotide infused into the amygdala disrupts fear conditioning. *Learn. Mem.* 11: 617-624, 2004.

Merlo, E., Freudenthal, R., Maldonado, H., Romano, A. Activation of the transcription factor NF-kappaB by retrieval is required for long-term memory reconsolidation. *Learn. Mem.* 12: 23-29, 2005.

Milekic, M.H., Alberini, C.M. Temporally graded requirement for protein synthesis following memory reactivation. *Neuron* 36: 521-525, 2002.

Nader, K., Schafe, G.E., LeDoux, J.E. Fear memories require protein synthesis in the amygdala for reconsolidation after retrieval. *Nature* 406: 722-726, 2000.

Nader, K., Hardt, O., Wang, S.H. Response to Alberini: right answer, wrong question. *Trends Neurosci.* 28: 346-347, 2005.

Sara, S.J. Retrieval and reconsolidation: toward a neurobiology of remembering. *Learn. Mem.* 7: 73-84, 2000.

Silva, A.J., Giese, K.P. Plastic genes are in! *Curr. Opin. Neurobiol.* 4: 413-420, 1994.

Stanciu, M., Radulovic, J., Spiess, J. Phosphorylated cAMP response element binding protein in the mouse brain after fear conditioning: relationship to Fos production. *Mol. Brain Res.* 94: 15-24, 2001.

Strekalova, T., Zorner, B., Zacher, C., Sadovska, G., Herdegen, T., Gass, P. Memory retrieval after contextual fear conditioning induces c-Fos and JunB expression in CA1 hippocampus. *Genes Brain Behav.* 2: 3-10, 2003.

Suzuki, A., Josselyn, S.A., Frankland, P.W., Masushige, S., Silva, A.J., Kida, S. Memory reconsolidation and extinction have distinct temporal and biochemical signatures. *J. Neurosci.* 24: 4787-4795, 2004.

Taubenfeld, S.M., Milekic, M.H., Monti, B., Alberini, C.M. The consolidation of new but not reactivated memory requires hippocampal C/EBPß. *Nat. Neurosci.* 4: 813- 818, 2001.

Tronel, S., Sara, S.J. Mapping of olfactory memory circuits: region-specific c-fos activation after odor-reward associative learning or after its retrieval. *Learn. Mem.* 9: 105-111, 2002.

von Hertzen, L.S.J., Giese, K.P. Memory reconsolidation engages only a subset of immediate-early genes induced during consolidation. *J. Neurosci.* 25: 1935-1942, 2005a.

von Hertzen, L.S.J., Giese, K.P. α-isoform of Ca^{2+}/calmodulin-dependent kinase II autophosphorylation is required for memory consolidation-specific transcription. *Neuroreport* 16: 1411-1414, 2005b.

In: Cognitive Sciences at the Leading Edge
Editor: Miao-Kun Sun, pp. 9-20

ISBN: 978-1-60456-051-0
© 2008 Nova Science Publishers, Inc.

Chapter 2

NEUROPROTECTIVE EFFECTS OF INSULIN-LIKE GROWTH FACTOR I AGAINST NEUROTOXIC AMYLOID

David Aguado-Llera[1,2], Eduardo Arilla-Ferreiro[2,]
Emma Burgos-Ramos[1], and Vicente Barrios[1,]*

[1] Department of Endocrinology, Hospital Infantil Universitario Niño Jesús,
Universidad Autónoma, E-28009 Madrid;
[2] Neurobiochemistry Unit, Universidad de Alcalá, E-28871 Alcalá de Henares, Spain

ABSTRACT

Alzheimer's disease (AD) is a neurodegenerative disorder anatomically characterized by the appearance of neurofibrillary tangles and extracellular deposits of amyloid peptides (Aβ). Although the primary alteration is not established, accumulative data indicate that deposition of Aβ in nerve terminals is the primary pathogenic event in this neurodegenerative process. Evidence indicates that glucose utilization is impaired in this disorder, suggesting that disruption of insulin and probably insulin-like growth factor I (IGF-I) signaling may be involved in the pathogenesis of AD. In this context, AD appears in the later periods of life when there is a progressive loss of sensitivity to IGF-I, as well as a decline in its circulating levels. In fact, decreased levels of IGF-I have been reported in familial forms of AD. However, high IGF-I and insulin levels are reported in the late onset form of this disease, reflecting a possible state of IGF-I resistance. Furthermore, animal models of familial AD suggest a disruption of IGF-I input that could be involved in Aβ accumulation. IGF-I is a physiologically important neurotrophic factor for both neurons and glial cells that is widely expressed in brain tissue early in development and, although reduced, this expression is maintained throughout adulthood. This growth factor possesses neurotrophic activities in areas severely affected in AD and its potential neuroprotective role could occur at least two levels. First, the activation of

---

* Corresponding author: Vicente Barrios, Ph.D., Department of Endocrinology, Hospital Infantil Universitario Niño Jesús, Avda. Menéndez Pelayo, 65, 28009 Madrid (Spain), Telephone: +34-91-5035900, Fax: +34-91-5035939, E-mail: vbarrios@telefonica.net

IGF-I receptors protects neurons against cell death induced by Aβ and IGF-I normalizes intracellular signaling pathways affected by Aβ. In this regard, IGF-I activates the phosphatidylinositol 3 kinase (PI3K)/Akt pathway, which is reduced in patients with a mutation of the Aβ precursor protein, and the Aβ induced increase in c-Jun kinase (JNK) is also blocked by IGF-I administration. In addition, given its capacity to modulate insulin actions, IGF-I may protect against the decrease in neuronal insulin sensitivity described in AD. Furthermore, IGF-I is reported to regulate brain Aβ levels by enhancing clearance of neurotoxic fragments, possibly by increasing the transport of Aβ carrier proteins such as albumin and transthyretin into the brain. Given that preliminary clinical trials show that treatment of insulin resistance in AD is beneficial and IGF-I infusion reduces brain Aβ deposits in mice over-expressing mutant Aβ, it follows that IGF-I could be a useful therapeutic agent for the treatment of AD.

Keywords: Alzheimer's disease, β-amyloid, insulin-like growth factor I, neuroprotection

1. THE ROLE OF IGF-I IN NORMAL BRAIN FUNCTION

Insulin-like growth factor I (IGF-I) mediates many of the effects of growth hormone (GH) in the control of somatic growth. This growth factor, localized in many tissues and body fluids, exerts trophic effects acting as an endocrine and paracrine/autocrine factor (Jones and Clemmons, 1995). IGF-I, its membrane receptor and the IGF-binding proteins (IGFBPs), are all widely found in brain tissue during development and their expression is maintained in different brain areas during adulthood (Torres-Alemán, 1999). Emerging evidence indicates that IGF-I has diverse and relevant functions in the brain, including metabolic, neuroendocrine, neurotrophic and neuromodulatory actions (Torres-Alemán, 2005). Thus, during development of the nervous system IGF-I promotes neuron differentiation, growth and survival (Lobie et al., 2000), whereas in the adult brain it performs a wide-spectrum of trophic and reparative actions.

Many of the functions of IGF-I overlap with those of insulin. In fact, both hormones belong to the same protein family (Mattson, 2002). One common function of insulin and IGF-I is that they both modulate brain function and energy balance (Bondy and Cheng, 2002). IGF-I and insulin bind to their own receptors with the highest affinity, but cross-reactivity occurs at higher hormone concentrations. Although these two factors have virtually identical signaling cascades, and many of their functions are common, they are not redundant. In fact, their distinct biological roles could be due to cell-specific expression patterns of receptors during development (Bondy and Cheng, 2004).

The actions of IGF-I are mediated by the IGF receptors and its biological activity is modulated through IGFBPs. The IGF-I receptor is a heterotetrameric membrane glycoprotein, that consists of two α- and two β-subunits and that binds IGF-I with higher affinity than IGF-II or insulin. After ligand binding to the α-subunits and activation of this tyrosine kinase receptor a variety of target molecules are phosphorylated, including its major substrate the insulin receptor substrate (IRS) proteins (Fig. 1). In turn, IRS phosphorylation activates growth-factor receptor-bound protein 2 (Grb2), the p85 regulatory subunit of phosphatidylinositol-3 kinase (PI3 kinase), phosphotyrosine phosphatases and transcription factors leading to modifications in calcium mobilization (Sun et. al, 1993; LeRoith et al., 1995), and subsequently changes in growth, metabolic functions and cell viability (Saltiel and

Pessin, 2002). Binding of IRS to Grb2 activates mitogen-activated protein kinase (MAPK), which contributes to mitogenesis, neurite development and modulation of gene expression (De la Monte and Wands, 2005). The association of IRS to p85 inhibits apoptosis through activation of PI3/Akt kinase (Dudek et al., 1997) and inhibition of glycogen synthase kinase-3β (GSK-3β) (Pap and Cooper, 1998). Akt kinase restrains apoptosis by phosphorylation of GSK-3β and Bad. Inactivation of Bad through this mechanism releases anti-apoptotic Bcl proteins and inhibits caspase activation, resulting in reduced neuronal death (Condorelli et al., 2001).

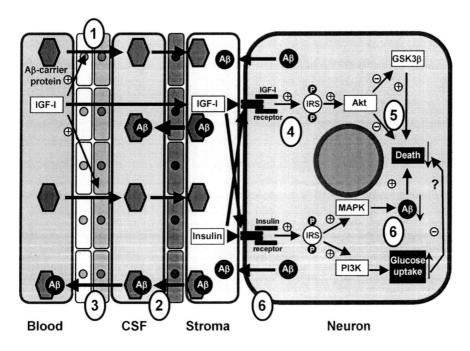

Figure 1. Roles for insulin-like growth factor I (IGF-I) against β-amyloid (Aβ). (1) Serum IGF-I stimulates the passage of Aβ-carrier proteins from the blood into the cerebrospinal fluid (CSF). (2) Aβ-carrier proteins accumulate in the brain stroma where they bind Aβ and transfer it into the CSF. (3) The complexes Aβ-Aβ carrier proteins are transported to the blood. (4) IGF-I binds to IGF-I and/or insulin receptors and induces phosphorylation of insulin receptor substrate (IRS). (5) IRS phosphorylation activates Akt that restrains apoptosis directly or indirectly through inhibition of glycogen synthetase kinase 3β (GSK3β), an enzyme that disrupts trafficking of Aβ and increases cell death. (6) IGF-I/insulin activation of mitogen-activated protein kinase (MAPK) promotes intracellular trafficking of Aβ to the plasma cell membrane. Phosphatidylinositol 3 kinase (PI3K) activation enhances glucose uptake and could increase cell survival.

2. ALZHEIMER'S DISEASE AND CEREBRAL AMYLOIDOSIS

Old age is a risk factor for important neurological impairments such as Alzheimer's disease (AD) and with the increased life span in modern societies the incidence of these conditions has also increased. This neurodegenerative disorder affects nearly 2% of the population in industrialized countries and the risk increases in subjects beyond the age of 70 (Mattson, 2004). Alzheimer's disease is characterized by plaques that represent extracellular deposition of amyloid β-peptide (Aβ), intraneuronal cytoskeletal abnormalities and increased neuronal death. An abnormally high level of Aβ in brain seems to have a central role in the pathogenesis of AD (Hardy and Selkoe, 2002), activating an inflammatory response that contributes to the increased cell death and the cognitive alterations that typify this disease (Walsh and Selkoe, 2004). Brain regions rich in these plaques are severely atrophic, in particular those involved in learning and memory processes such as the temporal and frontal lobes. The reduction in brain size in patients with AD is the result of degeneration of synapses and death of neurons (Mattson et al., 2001).

Aβ is a 39-43 amino acid peptide that originates from the proteolytic cleavage of the Aβ precursor protein (APP) (Selkoe, 1994), although fragments containing 25-35 amino acids have also been described (Kubo et al., 2002). Aberrant proteolytic processing of the Aβ precursor protein (APP) may promote neuronal degeneration by enhancing the concentrations of specific Aβ forms and diminishing the levels of the neuroprotective form of APP alpha (Kerr and Small, 2005). APP gene mutations are responsible for early onset AD (Goate et al., 1991), while in the more common sporadic forms of AD the initiating causes are unclear, but most likely involve increased levels of oxidative stress and impaired energy metabolism (Blass et al., 2002).

Elevated levels of Aβ are present in AD brains and its deposition inside the senile plaques is a hallmark of AD and appears to be a primary cause of the cognitive dysfunctions that occur. Indeed, Aβ-induced neuronal death could be responsible for the cognitive deterioration (Saura et al., 2005). In this context, Aβ administration increases cell death and leads to a significant reduction in p-Akt, a mechanism known to be involved in neuronal protection (Dudek et al., 1997). Indeed, this intracellular pathway has also been shown to be down-regulated in AD patients with altered forms of APP (Ryder et al., 2004). Another molecular mechanism by which Aβ induces toxicity has also been reported (Morishima et al., 2001). In this paradigm Aβ increases c-Jun N-terminal kinase (JNK) that then phosphorylates and activates the transcription factor c-Jun, which in turn stimulates the transcription of several genes including the death inducer Fas ligand. The binding of Fas to its receptor induces different signals leading to caspase activation and cell death. However, in spite of multiple data suggesting that Aβ deposition and neuronal loss are correlated, the direct link between Aβ production by neurons and cell death has only recently been clearly established.

3. IGF-I AND AMYLOIDOSIS

3.1. IGF-I in Alzheimer's Disease

We have previously shown that different neurodegenerative conditions have reduced levels of IGF-I in plasma and brain, both in humans (Torres-Alemán et al., 1996; Torres-Alemán et al., 1998) and in animal models (Busiguina et al., 2000), suggesting that IGF-I may be implicated in the ethiopathogenesis of these disorders. The pathogenic findings in AD suggest that many of the brain alterations may be related to impaired insulin/IGF-I signaling. Initial data in AD patients showed high serum IGF-I and IGFBP concentrations in the more common sporadic forms of AD (Tham et al., 1993) and low IGF-I levels in familial AD (Mustafa et al., 1999). Early studies seemed to indicate that IGF-I binding sites were augmented in cortical areas of the AD brain (Crews et al., 1992), but subsequent studies showed similar IGF-I binding in control and AD brains (Jafferali et al., 2000). In spite of these contradictory data, the concept of IGF-I resistance in AD should still be considered. First, despite normal or increased IGF-I/insulin receptor expression, tyrosine kinase activity in the brain is reduced in AD (Frolich et al., 1999). Second, the compensatory increase in IGF-I levels in late-onset AD patients (Tham et al., 1993) could indicate a loss in sensitivity to IGF-I, as does the progressive decrease in IGF-I sensitivity during aging (Willis et al., 1997), which occurs at the same time of AD appearance (Mrak et al., 1997). Third, as Aβ can bind to the insulin receptor (Xie et al., 2002), it is possible that it modulates IGF-I signaling by also competing for IGF-I binding sites. Four, Aβ could modulate IGF-I actions indirectly through cytokines, such as TNF-α, that induce IGF-I resistance. In this regard Aβ may lead to an inflammatory response by activation of mechanisms involving glial cells (Venters et al., 1999). Lastly, extensive abnormalities in IGF-I signaling mechanisms in AD brains have been reported including reduced levels of IRS mRNA, IRS-associated PI3 kinase and the activated form of Akt (p-Akt), as well as increased GSK-3β activity (Steen et al., 2005). Overall, disrupted IGF-I signaling may be considered as one of the primary events in sporadic forms of AD, which is the most common form of this disease.

3.2. IGF-I modulates Neurotoxicity and Brain Levels of Aβ

The protective functions of IGF-I against Aβ may occur through different mechanisms. Some neuroprotective actions of IGF-I could be regarded as independent of Aβ modulation and involve counteraction of amyloid effects. Preliminary *in vitro* studies demonstrated that activation of the IGF-I receptor in rat hippocampal neurons protects and rescues neurons against cell death induced by Aβ (Doré et al., 1997). Interestingly, IGF-I activates intracellular signaling pathways decreased by Aβ accumulation (Fig. 1). We have shown that subcutaneous IGF-I administration increases the levels of p-Akt in the temporal cortex of Aβ-treated rats (Aguado-Llera et al., 2005) and p-Akt has been shown to be down-regulated in AD patients with APP mutations (Ryder et al., 2004). Another mechanism by which IGF-I could suppress Aβ neurotoxicity is through the JNK pathway (Wei et al., 2002). JNK, which is triggered in response to stress signals, is increased in response to Aβ and IGF-I protects against Aβ-induced cell death by blocking JNK activation. In addition, IGF-I may exert its neuroprotective properties through the tripeptide Gly-Pro-Glu (GPE), which is naturally cleaved from the N-terminal sequence of IGF-I (Sara et al., 1989). Both GPE and IGF-I molecules have a beneficial effect in restoring at least one neurotransmitter system severely affected by Aβ insult (Aguado-Llera et al., 2004; Aguado-Llera et al., 2005). However, IGF-I actions are not specific to Aβ-induced cell death, as a similar effect has been described after ethanol exposure. Indeed, neuronal rescue from toxic effects of ethanol is also mediated by IGF-I activation of Akt (De la Monte et al., 2000).

Another mechanism by which IGF-I may exert its neuroprotective effects is through modulation of Aβ levels. At a cellular level, IGF-I imitates insulin in its capacity to increase Aβ release from neurons, but it is not clear whether IGF-I and insulin act through the same receptor to modulate Aβ release (Gasparini et al., 2001). IGF-I activation of extracellular signal-regulated kinase (ERK) MAPK promotes physiological trafficking of Aβ to the plasma cell membrane (Fig. 1). Furthermore, oxidative stress caused by increased GSK-3β disrupts intracellular trafficking of Aβ and IGF-I reduces GSK-3β activity (Pap and Cooper, 1998). An additional mechanism could involve an IGF-I-mediated increase of neuronal excitability (Núñez et al., 2003), as formation and secretion of Aβ in neurons that over-express APP is enhanced by neuronal activity. In turn, Aβ peptides depress excitatory synaptic transmission in the same neurons (Kamenetz et al., 2003).

At the organ level, IGF-I appears to be a major regulator of brain Aβ peptide concentrations through a mechanism involving a network of Aβ transport proteins interacting at the blood-brain barrier (Carro et al., 2002). IGF-I enhances brain levels of carrier proteins such as transthyretin, albumin and apolipoprotein J and promotes clearance of Aβ from the brain parenchyma (Fig. 1). This IGF-I induced reduction in Aβ levels appears to be due to an increase in the Aβ clearance rate, as IGF-I administration increases Aβ levels in cerebrospinal fluid, enhances the formation of Aβ/carrier protein complexes and does not modify APP concentrations (Carro and Torres-Alemán, 2004a). Treatment with IGF-I reduces amyloidosis in advanced stages of the process, not only because its administration inhibits Aβ accumulation, but it also eliminates previously developed deposits (Carro et al., 2005).

4. POTENTIAL FUNCTION OF IGF-I IN THE TREATMENT OF ALZHEIMER'S DISEASE

Currently cholinesterase inhibitors are the only drugs widely recommended for clinical use in AD, although the average benefit appears to be small. These drugs provide moderate cognitive protection and induce unwanted sleep disturbances (Potyk, 2005) and anti-amyloidal vaccine trials had undesirable effects. It is known that chronic neuroinflammation contributes to AD and vaccination with Aβ in mouse models of AD stimulated phagocytosis of the toxic peptides and gave optimal results, but similar vaccination in humans led to meningoencephalitis in some cases (McGeer and McGeer, 2004).

The amyloid overload in AD patients may be regarded as the result of increased amyloid deposition as compared to age-matched normal subjects. In this context, decreased IGF-I signaling and lower levels of Aβ carrier proteins in AD patients (Serot et al., 1997) could lead to increased Aβ levels in these patients. Stimulating IGF-I signaling could provide neuroprotection by increasing Aβ clearance, counteracting TNFα effects and decreasing inflammatory reactions (Gasparini and Xu, 2003). In addition, IGF-I could be safely administered systemically and continuous subcutaneous infusion would avoid hypoglycemia (Woodall et al., 1991). However, one of the major counter-indication is that IGF-I, due the its typical growth promoting actions, could advance the progression of some forms of cancer (Yakar et al., 2005). Because endogenous IGF-I could be an approach for Alzheimer's treatment the use of GH, the classical stimulator of IGF-I production, should be further investigated. In contrast to exogenous IGF-I treatment this hormone has been used therapeutically for over 20 years and the therapeutic profile is well verified. Indeed, GH treatment has been used in patients with amyotrophic lateral sclerosis, showing a benefit with scarce adverse effects (Smith et al., 1993). Other possible approaches are the use of IGF-I analogs that bind to IGFBPs displacing IGF-I and increasing its bioavailability or alternative secretagogues, such as imidazolines (Hoy et al., 2003), that appear to increase circulating IGF-I levels (Loddick et al., 1998; Carro and Torres-Alemán, 2004b).

Studies of the mechanisms implicated in Aβ-induced neuronal degeneration have led to the discovery of several peptides reported to prevent neuron death. One of these peptides is GPE, which is cleaved from the IGF-I molecule and protects against hypoxic-ischemic injury (Sizonenko et al., 2001). We have previously demonstrated that GPE protects the somatostatinergic system from Aβ insult (Aguado-Llera et al., 2004) and interestingly, a GPE analog reduces neuronal degeneration by preventing Aβ-mediated apoptosis (Ioudina and Uemura, 2003). These neuroprotective effects, independent of interaction with IGF receptors (Sara et al., 1993), suggest a novel and promising strategy toward treatment of patients with AD.

Recently, a clinical trial with donepezil, a cerebral selective cholinesterase inhibitor that improves cognitive symptoms in AD patients (Harry and Zakzanis, 2005), was reported to increase circulating IGF-I levels (Obermayr et al., 2005). This result suggests that the age-related down-regulation of the IGF-I axis, reverted by this drug, could be of importance in the treatment of AD patients. Clinical trials have also suggested beneficial effects of IGF-I in the treatment of peripheral neurodegenerative disease, with little side effects seen (Vlachopapadopoulou et al., 1995; Lai et al., 1997). In addition, treatment with IGF-I is effective in animal models of cerebellar ataxia (Fernández et al., 2005) and ischemia (Loddick et al. 1998). These promising results suggest that the IGF-I signaling pathway could represent a therapeutic target for the treatment of neurodegenerative diseases.

CONCLUSION

Disruption of normal IGF-I signaling is involved in the deposition of Aβ (Wei et al, 2002), which appears to initiate the pathological cascade leading to AD (Selkoe, 2001). Indeed, IGF-I has shown its efficacy in the treatment of some peripheral neurodegenerative disorders (Lai et al., 1997). As this growth factor modulates neurotoxicity and levels of Aβ (Carro et al., 2002), it could be considered as a possible therapeutic agent for the treatment of AD.

ACKNOWLEDGEMENTS

The authors wish to thank Dr. Julie A. Chowen for the critical review of the manuscript. Supported by Grant PI021241 from the Fondo de Investigación Sanitaria and Fundación Endocrinología y Nutrición.

REFERENCES

Aguado-Llera, D., Arilla-Ferreiro, E., Campos-Barros, A., Puebla-Jiménez, L. and Barrios, V. Protective effects of insulin-like growth factor-I on the somatostatinergic system in the temporal cortex of β-amyloid-treated rats. *J. Neurochem.* 92: 607-615, 2005.

Aguado-Llera, D., Martín-Martínez, M., García-López, M.T., Arilla-Ferreiro, E. and Barrios V. Gly-Pro-Glu protects β-amyloid-induced somatostatin depletion in the rat cortex. *Neuroreport* 15: 1979-1982, 2004.

Blass, J.P., Gibson, G.E. and Hoyer S. The role of the metabolic lesion in Alzheimer's disease. *J. Alzheimers Dis.* 4: 225-232, 2002.

Bondy, C.A. and Cheng C.M. Insulin-like growth factor-1 promotes neuronal glucose utilization during brain development and repair processes. *Int. Rev. Neurobiol.* 51: 189-217, 2002.

Bondy, C.A. and Cheng C.M. Signaling by insulin-like growth factor 1 in brain. *Eur. J. Pharmacol.* 490: 25-31, 2004.

Busiguina, S., Fernández, A.M., Barrios, V., Clark, R., Tolbert, D.L., Berciano, J. and Torres-Alemán, I. Neurodegeneration is associated to changes in serum insulin-like growth factors. *Neurobiol. Dis.* 7: 657-665, 2000.

Carro, E. and Torres-Alemán, I. The role of insulin and insulin-like growth factor I in the molecular and cellular mechanisms underlying the pathology of Alzheimer's disease. *Eur. J. Pharmacol.* 490: 127-133, 2004a.

Carro, E. and Torres-Alemán, I. Insulin-like growth factor I and Alzheimer's disease: therapeutic prospects?. *Expert Rev. Neurother.* 4: 79-86, 2004b.

Carro, E., Trejo, J.L., Gerber, A., Loetscher, H., Torrado, J., Metzger, F. and Torres-Alemán, I. Therapeutic actions of insulin-like growth factor I on APP/PS2 mice with severe brain amyloidosis. *Neurobiol. Aging.* 27: 1250-1257, 2006.

Carro, E., Trejo, J.L., Gómez-Isla, T., LeRoith, D. and Torres-Alemán, I. Serum insulin-like growth factor I regulates brain amyloid-β levels. *Nat. Med.* 8: 1390-1397, 2002.

Condorelli, F., Salomoni, P., Cotteret, S., Cesi, V., Srinivasula, S.M., Alnemri, E.S. and Calabretta, B. Caspase cleavage enhances the apoptosis-inducing effects of BAD. *Mol. Cell. Biol.* 21: 3025-3036, 2001.

De la Monte, S.M., Ganju, N., Banerjee, K., Brown, N.V., Luong, T. and Wands, J.R. Partial rescue of ethanol-induced neuronal apoptosis by growth factor activation of phosphoinositol-3-kinase. *Alcohol Clin. Exp.* Res. 24: 716-726, 2000.

De la Monte, S.M. and Wands, J.R. Review of insulin and insulin-like growth factor expression, signaling, and malfunction in the central nervous system: relevance to Alzheimer's disease. *J. Alzheimers Dis.* 7: 45-61, 2005.

Doré, S., Kar, S. and Quirion, R. Insulin-like growth factor I protects and rescues hippocampal neurons against β-amyloid- and human amylin-induced toxicity. *Proc. Natl. Acad. Sci. USA* 94: 4772-4777, 1997.

Dudek, H., Datta, S.R., Franke, T.F., Birnbaum, M.J., Yao, R., Cooper, G.M., Segal, R.A., Kaplan, D.R. and Greenberg M.E. Regulation of neuronal survival by the serine-threonine protein kinase *Akt. Science* 275: 661-665, 1997.

Fernández, A.M., Carro, E.M., López-López, C. and Torres-Alemán, I. Insulin-like growth factor I treatment for cerebellar ataxia: Addressing a common pathway in the pathological cascade? *Brain Res. Brain Res.* Rev. 50: 134-141, 2005.

Frolich, L., Blum-Degen, D., Riederer, P. and Hoyer, S. A disturbance in the neuronal insulin receptor signal transduction in sporadic Alzheimer's disease. *Ann. N.Y. Acad. Sci.* 893: 290-293, 1999.

Gasparini, L., Gouras, G.K., Wang, R., Gross, R.S., Beal, M.F., Greengard, P. and Xu, H. Stimulation of β-amyloid precursor protein trafficking by insulin reduces intraneuronal β-amyloid and requires mitogen-activated protein kinase signaling. *J. Neurosci.* 21: 2561-2570, 2001.

Gasparini, L. and Xu, H. Potential roles of insulin and IGF-1 in Alzheimer's disease. *Trends Neurosci.* 26: 404-406, 2003.

Goate, A., Chartier-Harlin, M.C., Mullan, M., Brown, J., Crawford, F., Fidani, L., Giuffra, L., Haynes A., Irving, N., James, L., Mant, R., Newton, P., Rooke, K., Roques, P., Talbot C., Pericak-Vance, M., Roses, A., Williamson, R., Rossor, M., Owen, M. and Hardy, J. Segregation of a missense mutation in the amyloid precursor protein gene with familial Alzheimer's disease. *Nature* 349: 704-706, 1991.

Hardy, J. and Selkoe, D.J. The amyloid hypothesis of Alzheimer's disease: progress and problems on the road of therapeutics. *Science* 297: 353-356, 2002.

Harry, R.D. and Zakzanis K.K. A comparison of donepezil and galantamine in the treatment of cognitive symptoms of Alzheimer's disease: a meta-analysis. *Hum. Psychopharmacol.* 20: 183-187, 2005.

Hoy, M., Olsen, H.L., Andersen, H.S., Bokvist, K., Buschard, K., Hansen, J., Jacobsen, P., Petersen, J.S., Rorsman, P. and Gromada J. Imidazoline NNC77-0074 stimulates insulin secretion and inhibits glucagon release by control of Ca(2+)-dependent exocytosis in pancreatic α- and β-cells. *Eur. J. Pharmacol.* 466: 213-221, 2003.

Ioudina, M. and Uemura, E. A three amino acid peptide, Gly-Pro-Arg, protects and rescues cell death induced by amyloid β-peptide. *Exp. Neurol.* 184: 923-929, 2003.

Jafferali, S., Dumont, Y., Sotty, F., Robitaille, Y., Quirion, R. and Kar S. Insulin-like growth factor-I and its receptor in the frontal cortex, hippocampus, and cerebellum of normal human and alzheimer disease brains. *Synapse* 38: 450-459, 2000.

Jones, J.I. and Clemmons, D.R. Insulin-like growth factors and their binding proteins: biological actions. *Endocr. Rev.* 16: 3-34, 1995.

Kamenetz, F., Tomita, T., Hsieh, H., Seabrook, G., Borchelt, D., Iwatsubo, T., Sisodia, S. and Malinow, R. APP processing and synaptic function. *Neuron* 37: 925-937, 2003.

Kerr, M.L. and Small, D.H. Cytoplasmic domain of the beta-amyloid protein precursor of Alzheimer's disease: function, regulation of proteolysis, and implications for drug development. *J. Neurosci. Res.* 80: 151-159, 2005.

Kubo, T., Nishimura, S., Kumagae, Y. and Kaneko I. In vivo conversion of racemized β-amyloid ([D-Ser 26]A β 1-40) to truncated and toxic fragments ([D-Ser 26]A β 25-35/40) and fragment presence in the brains of Alzheimer's patients. *J. Neurosci. Res.* 70: 474-483, 2002.

Lai, E.C., Felice, K.J., Festoff, B.W., Gawel, M.J., Gelinas, D.F., Kratz, R., Murphy, M.F., Natter H.M., Norris, F.H. and Rudnicki, S.A. Effect of recombinant human insulin-like growth factor-I on progression of ALS. A placebo-controlled study. The North America ALS/IGF-I Study Group. *Neurology* 49: 1621-1630, 1997.

LeRoith, D., Werner, H., Beitner-Johnson, D. and Roberts C.T. Jr. Molecular and cellular aspects of the insulin-like growth factor I receptor. *Endocr. Rev.* 16: 143-163, 1995.

Lobie, P,E, Zhu, T., Graichen, R. and Goh, E.L. Growth hormone, insulin-like growth factor I and the CNS: localization, function and mechanism of action. *Growth Horm. IGF Res.* 10 (Suppl B): S51-56, 2000.

Loddick, S.A., Liu, X.J., Lu, Z.X., Liu, C., Behan, D.P., Chalmers, D.C., Foster, A.C., Vale, W.W., Ling, N. and De Souza, E.B. Displacement of insulin-like growth factors from their binding proteins as a potential treatment for stroke. *Proc. Natl. Acad. Sci. USA 95*: 1894-1898, 1998.

Mattson, M.P. Brain evolution and lifespan regulation: conservation of signal transduction pathways that regulate energy metabolism. *Mech. Ageing Dev.* 123: 947-953, 2002.

Mattson, M.P. Pathways towards and away from Alzheimer's disease. *Nature* 430: 631-639, 2004.

Mattson, M.P., Gary, D.S., Chan, S.L. and Duan, W. Perturbed endoplasmic reticulum function, synaptic apoptosis and the pathogenesis of Alzheimer's disease. *Biochem. Soc. Symp.* 67: 151-162, 2001.

McGeer, P.L. and McGeer, E. Immunotherapy for Alzheimer's disease. Sci. *Aging Knowledge Environ.* 27: 29, 2004.

Morishima, Y., Gotoh, Y., Zieg, J., Barrett, T., Takano, H., Flavell, R., Davis, R.J., Shirasaki, Y. and Greenberg M.E. β-amyloid induces neuronal apoptosis via a mechanism that involves the c-Jun N-terminal kinase pathway and the induction of Fas ligand. *J. Neurosci.* 21: 7551-7560, 2001.

Mrak, R.E., Griffin, S.T. and Graham, D.I. Aging-associated changes in human brain. *J. Neuropathol. Exp. Neurol.* 56: 1269-1275, 1997.

Mustafa, A., Lannfelt, L., Lilius, L., Islam, A., Winblad, B. and Adem, A. Decreased plasma insulin-like growth factor-I level in familial Alzheimer's disease patients carrying the Swedish APP 670/671 mutation. *Dement. Geriatr. Cogn. Disord.* 10: 446-451, 1999.

Núñez, A., Carro, E. and Torres-Alemán, I. Insulin-like growth factor I modifies electrophysiological properties of rat brain stem neurons. *J Neurophysiol.* 89: 3008-3017, 2003.

Obermayr, R.P., Mayerhofer, L., Knechtelsdorfer, M., Mersich, N., Huber, E.R., Geyer, G. and Tragl, K.H. The age-related down-regulation of the growth hormone/insulin-like growth factor-1 axis in the elderly male is reversed considerably by donepezil, a drug for Alzheimer's disease. *Exp. Gerontol.* 40: 157-163, 2005.

Pap, M. and Cooper G.M. Role of glycogen synthase kinase-3 in the phosphatidylinositol 3-Kinase/Akt cell survival pathway. *J. Biol. Chem.* 273: 19929-19932, 1998.

Potyk, D. Treatments for Alzheimer disease. *South Med. J.* 98: 628-635, 2005.

Ryder, J., Su, Y. and Ni, B. Akt/GSK3beta serine/threonine kinases: evidence for a signalling pathway mediated by familial Alzheimer's disease mutations. *Cell Signal.* 16: 187-200, 2004.

Saltiel, A.R. and Pessin, J.E. Insulin signaling pathways in time and space. *Trends Cell. Biol.* 12: 65-71, 2002.

Sara, V.R., Carlsson-Skwirut, C., Bergman, T., Jornvall, H., Roberts, P.J., Crawford, M., Hakansson, L.N., Civalero, I. and Nordberg, A. Identification of Gly-Pro-Glu (GPE), the aminoterminal tripeptide of insulin-like growth factor 1 which is truncated in brain, as a novel neuroactive peptide. *Biochem. Biophys. Res. Commun.* 165: 766-771, 1989.

Sara, V.R., Carlsson-Skwirut, C., Drakenberg, K., Giacobini, M.B., Hakansson, L., Mirmiran, M., Nordberg, A., Olson, L., Reinecke, M., Stahlbom, P.A. and Nordqvist, A.C.S. The biological role of truncated insulin-like growth factor-1 and the tripeptide GPE in the central nervous system. *Ann. NY Acad. Sci.* 692: 183-191, 1993.

Saura, C.A., Chen, G., Malkani, S., Choi, S.Y., Takahashi, R.H., Zhang, D., Gouras, G.K., Kirkwood, A., Morris R.G. and Shen J. Conditional inactivation of presenilin 1 prevents amyloid accumulation and temporarily rescues contextual and spatial working memory impairments in amyloid precursor protein transgenic mice. *J. Neurosci.* 25: 6755-6764, 2005.

Selkoe, D.J. Normal and abnormal biology of the β-amyloid precursor protein. *Annu. Rev. Neurosci.* 17: 489-517, 1994.

Selkoe, D.J. Clearing the brain's amyloid cobwebs. Neuron 32: 177-180, 2001.

Serot, J.M., Christmann, D., Dubost, T. and Couturier, M. Cerebrospinal fluid transthyretin: aging and late onset Alzheimer's disease. *J. Neurol. Neurosurg. Psychiatry* 63: 506-508, 1997.

Sizonenko, S.V., Sirimanne, E.S., Williams, C.E. and Gluckman P.D. Neuroprotective effects of the N-terminal tripeptide of IGF-1, glycine-proline-glutamate, in the immature rat brain after hypoxic-ischemic injury. *Brain Res.* 922: 42-50, 2001.

Smith, R.A., Melmed, S., Sherman, B., Frane, J., Munsat, T.L. and Festoff B.W. Recombinant growth hormone treatment of amyotrophic lateral sclerosis. *Muscle Nerve* 16: 624-633, 1993.

Steen, E., Terry, B.M., Rivera, E.J., Cannon, J.L., Neely, T.R., Tavares, R., Xu, X.J., Wands, J.R. and de la Monte, S.M. Impaired insulin and insulin-like growth factor expression and signaling mechanisms in Alzheimer's disease-is this type 3 diabetes? *J. Alzheimers Dis.* 7: 63-80, 2005

Sun, X.J., Crimmins, D.L., Myers, M.G. Jr, Miralpeix, M. and White M.F. Pleiotropic insulin signals are engaged by multisite phosphorylation of IRS-1. *Mol. Cell. Biol.* 13: 7418-7428, 1993.

Tham, A., Nordberg, A., Grissom, F.E., sulin signals are engaged by multisite phosphorylation of IRS-1. MolCarlsson-Skwirut, C., Viitanen, M. and Sara, V.R. Insulin-like growth factors and insulin-like growth factor binding proteins in cerebrospinal fluid and serum of patients with dementia of the Alzheimer type. *J. Neural Transm. Park. Dis. Dement. Sect.* 5: 165-176, 1993.

Torres-Alemán, I. Insulin-like growth factors as mediators of functional plasticity in the adult brain. *Horm. Metab. Res.* 31: 114-119, 1999.

Torres-Alemán, I. Role of insulin-like growth factors in neuronal plasticity and neuroprotection. Valera-Nieto I., Chowen J.A. (Eds.), The growth hormone/insulin-like growth factor axis during development. *Advances in Experimental Medicine and Biology*, Vol. 567, pp. 243-258, Springer, New York, 2005.

Torres-Alemán, I., Barrios, V. and Berciano, J. The peripheral insulin-like growth factor system in amyotrophic lateral sclerosis and in multiple sclerosis. *Neurology* 50: 772-776, 1998.

Torres-Alemán, I., Barrios, V., Lledó, A. and Berciano, J. The insulin-like growth factor I system in cerebellar degeneration. *Ann. Neurol.* 39: 335-342, 1996.

Venters, H.D., Tang, Q., Liu, Q., VanHoy, R.W., Dantzer, R. and Kelley, K.W. A new mechanism of neurodegeneration: a proinflammatory cytokine inhibits receptor signaling by a survival peptide. *Proc. Natl. Acad. Sci. USA* 96: 9879-9884, 1999.

Vlachopapadopoulou, E., Zachwieja, J.J., Gertner, J.M., Manzione, D., Bier, D.M., Matthews, D.E. and Slonim A.E. Metabolic and clinical response to recombinant human insulin-like growth factor I in myotonic dystrophy: a clinical research center study. *J. Clin. Endocrinol. Metab.* 80: 3715-3723, 1995.

Walsh, D.M. and Selkoe, D.J. Deciphering the molecular basis of memory failure in Alzheimer's disease. *Neuron* 44: 181-193, 2004.

Wei, W., Wang, X. and Kusiak, J.W. Signaling events in amyloid β-peptide-induced neuronal death and insulin-like growth factor I protection. *J. Biol. Chem.* 277: 17649-17656, 2002.

Willis, P.E., Chadan, S., Baracos, V. and Parkhouse, W.S. Acute exercise attenuates age-associated resistance to insulin-like growth factor I. *Am. J. Physiol.* 272: E397-404, 1997.

Woodall, S.M., Breier, B.H., O'Sullivan, U. and Gluckman, P.D. The effect of the frequency of subcutaneous insulin-like growth factor-1 administration on weight gain in growth hormone deficient mice. *Horm. Metab. Res.* 23: 581-584, *1991*.

Yakar, S., Leroith, D. and Brodt, P. The role of the growth hormone/insulin-like growth factor axis in tumor growth and progression: Lessons from animal models. *Cytokine Growth Factor Rev.* 16: 407-420, 2005.

In: Cognitive Sciences at the Leading Edge
Editor: Miao-Kun Sun, pp. 21-32

ISBN: 978-1-60456-051-0
© 2008 Nova Science Publishers, Inc.

Chapter 3

HOW AND WHERE DOES Aβ EXERT ITS TOXIC EFFECTS IN ALZHEIMER'S DISEASE?

Damian C. Crowther, Richard M. Page*†, Leila Luheshi and David A. Lomas*

Department of Medicine, University of Cambridge,
Cambridge Institute for Medical
Research, Wellcome Trust/MRC Building, Hills Road,
Cambridge, CB2 2XY, U.K. and
†University Chemical Laboratory, Lensfield Road,
Cambridge CB2 1EW, U.K.

INTRODUCTION

Protein aggregation is the basis for many of the common human neurodegenerative diseases such as Alzheimer's disease (AD), Parkinson's disease and a family of disorders that includes Huntington's disease. In AD the aggregatory species is termed amyloid β (Aβ), a peptide derived from the proteolytic cleavage of amyloid precursor protein (APP), a ubiquitous transmembrane protein. The aggregatory properties of Aβ are determined by variations in the position of the proteolytic cleavage that generates the C-terminus. In healthy elderly individuals the ratio of the 40 amino acid peptide ($A\beta_{1-40}$) to the 42 amino acid species ($A\beta_{1-42}$) favours the less aggregatory $A\beta_{1-40}$ resulting in effective clearance of the peptide from the brain. In contrast, individuals who go on to develop the common sporadic form of AD have elevated $A\beta_{1-42}$ concentrations, or have a molar ratio of $A\beta_{1-40}$ to $A\beta_{1-42}$ that favours aggregation. In the five percent of AD cases that are inherited as an autosomal dominant trait all the causal mutations have been shown to favour Aβ aggregation, mostly by altering APP processing, either increasing $A\beta_{1-42}$ in absolute terms or in comparison to $A\beta_{1-40}$. In rare examples, where $A\beta_{1-42}$ levels are not elevated, mutations are found within the Aβ sequence

* These authors contributed equally. Correspondence should be addressed to D.C.C.:Email: dcc26@cam.ac.uk. Telephone: 44 1223 336825. Fax: 44 1223 336827

that accelerate the intrinsic rate of peptide aggregation and stabilise particularly toxic subpopulations of aggregates, a clear example of this is the Arctic APP mutation [1, 2].

In the context of cognitive decline, the demonstration of Aβ deposition in the brain in combination with intraneuronal aggregates of a microtubule-associated protein, tau, comprise the diagnostic criteria for AD. Mature deposits of Aβ are composed of ordered amyloid fibrils and it is their distinctive microscopic appearance and their affinity for dyes such as Congo red that favoured their early characterisation. However there is a poor correlation between the burden of amyloid plaques and the degree of cognitive impairment, indeed elderly individuals may have many plaques without showing signs of cognitive impairment [3-5]. In contrast, it is the intracellular tau pathology that has been shown to correlate more closely with clinical deficits. The location and progression of the tau lesions correlates well with the brain areas, such as the hippocampus, that are particularly impaired in AD [6].

The poor correlation between extracellular amyloid plaques and dementia has been used to detract from the significance of Aβ in the pathogenesis of AD. However recent evidence has clarified the situation, emphasising the toxic role of small Aβ aggregates rather than the amyloid fibrils. The finding that soluble Aβ correlates better with synaptic changes and cognitive deficits than plaque count [7-9] has prompted the investigation of soluble aggregates of Aβ. These small aggregates can be purified by column chromatography and are composed of as few as 4 [10] or as many as 180 [2] Aβ molecules. When applied to cell cultures the oligomers are toxic whereas in most cases amyloid fibrils and Aβ monomers are not [11, 12]. When oligomers are visualised under electron or atomic force microscopes they are heterogeneous, including spheres, beads-on-a-string and doughnuts [2], but it seems that the spherical species are most toxic [13]. Toxic oligomers may also be specifically detected, *in vitro* and *in vivo*, using rabbit antisera raised against Aβ immobilised on gold beads. The antiserum, described by Kayed and colleagues [14], binds specifically to small toxic aggregates of Aβ and neutralises their toxicity, in contrast the serum fails to detect monomeric or fibrillar forms of Aβ. Subsequent work has shown that the antiserum recognises an epitope on Aβ oligomers that is common to the oligomeric aggregates of a range of pathological proteins. The interesting corollary of this observation is that a common structural motif predicts a common mechanism of toxicity. This prediction is supported by work by Bucciantini *et al.* showing that oligomeric aggregates of a non disease related protein can elicit toxicity similar to that of Aβ oligomers in cell culture [15]. Further work done in cell culture by Demuro and colleagues [16] has shown that a shared ability to disturb membrane conductivity may underlie at least part of the toxicity of soluble protein aggregates.

However the hypothesis that soluble aggregates of Aβ represent a stable neurotoxic species has had to be reconsidered in the light of recent work showing that it is the ongoing *process* of aggregation that is toxic. It seems now that the soluble aggregates may simply be an efficient seed that can promote further addition of Aβ monomers. In their recent study, Wogulis and colleagues showed that, as expected, neither monomeric nor fibrillar Aβ were toxic to human or rat neuronal cell cultures. Their novel observation was that pre-treatment of cells with fibrillar Aβ, followed by a wash to remove unbound fibrils, primed the cells to die when they were subsequently treated with monomeric Aβ. The stability of the interaction of the fibrils with the cells was a surprise; following exposure to fibrils for only one hour the cells were still sensitized to the toxic effects of monomeric Aβ one week later [17].

With emphasis being placed on the oligomeric aggregates and the initial stages of the aggregation process, the mature plaques and tangles are increasingly being viewed as tombstones of pathological protein aggregation. Indeed there is evidence from cell-based models of Parkinson's disease that inclusions may be protective, reducing the rate of apoptosis [18] possibly by providing a sink for the disposal of toxic oligomers.

INTRANEURONAL Aβ$_{1-42}$ ACCUMULATION AND AGGREGATION

The classical view of APP processing is that Aβ is generated and released at the cell surface, resulting in extracellular amyloid plaque deposition and neurotoxicity. However it well documented that the machinery for generating Aβ exists intracellularly [19-22]. Some investigators have emphasised the importance of the secretory pathway in generating Aβ by showing that the treatment of cells with inhibitors of vesicular transport that effectively block APP export from the endoplasmic reticulum [20] or trans-Golgi network [21] do not abolish Aβ generation. Moreover APP processing in the endoplasmic reticulum preferentially yields Aβ$_{1-42}$ [22-24] that remains intracellular, whereas Aβ$_{1-40}$ is preferentially generated in the trans-Golgi network and packaged into secretory vesicles. There is also evidence that APP is processed after it has reached the plasma membrane and that endocytosis is important for the generation of Aβ [25]. This is of particular note because the low pH of the endosomes/lysosomes compartment will predictably favour oligomer formation [26, 27]. However there is the possibility that intracellular Aβ exerts at least part of its toxicity, not from the aqueous environment of vesicle lumen, but from within the membrane itself. There is evidence that Aβ peptides are sequestered in membranes predominantly as dimers [28] and some workers have proposed that specific intramembraneous protein-protein interactions may mediate some of the toxic effects of Aβ [29].

Aβ oligomerisation has been shown to start intracellularly in cell culture [30] and oligomers are present in the brains of patients with AD [10]. Clinical specimens have also shown that Aβ is intracellular during the early stages of AD but becomes predominantly extracellular as the patient develops advanced disease [31]. It may be that intracellular Aβ disappears with time because heavily-burdened neurones die, releasing their aggregates; indeed studies looking at the distribution and morphology of amyloid plaques suggest that each amyloid plaque is the result of a single neuronal lysis event [32].

The history of AD research has shown that good animal models have helped enormously to accelerate our understanding. The most recent animal models of Alzheimer's disease are providing strong support for the role of intracellular Aβ in generating the earliest symptoms of Alzheimer's disease [33, 34]. Triple transgenic mice that express disease-causing mutants of human APP, presenilin-1 and tau demonstrate clearly that intraneuronal accumulation of Aβ is sufficient to cause the earliest cognitive deficits [35]. At an age of four months the mice exhibit impaired long-term memory retention at a stage when plaques, tau pathology and neuronal death are entirely absent but intracellular Aβ is present. The presence of intracellular accumulation of Aβ may also explain why these triple transgenic mice are the first to show convincing neuronal loss as well as dysfunction [34]. This work in mouse models is supported by recent *Drosophila* models of AD that demonstrate non-amyloid intracellular Aβ aggregates are sufficient to cause locomotor deficits before extracellular Aβ deposits or cell death are seen [36]. Treating model organisms with anti-aggregatory compounds [36] or antibodies to Aβ [35] can ameliorate or even reverse the neuronal dysfunction that results from intraneuronal Aβ.

WHAT IS THE ROLE OF EXTRACELLULAR Aβ?

Extracellular Aβ has a wide range of effects that can be divided into two main categories. Firstly, Aβ has sequence-specific interactions with other proteins; notable is the binding of Aβ to receptors that are normally involved in the clearance of the peptide from the brain. Aβ also interacts specifically with receptors involved in neurotransmission and may cause some of the early, potentially reversible, symptoms of AD. Secondly, Aβ has biophysical effects on the electrical properties of membranes and also promotes oxidative stress, both of which contribute to the neuronal death seen in established cases of AD.

THE INTERACTION OF EXTRACELLULAR Aβ
WITH THE CLEARANCE PATHWAYS

The concentration of Aβ in the brain depends both on the rate of production of the peptide and on the efficiency of the clearance mechanisms. Although the bulk of human genetic evidence points to the primary importance of Aβ synthesis in causing familial disease (presenilin 1 and 2 and APP mutations), there is some evidence that polymorphisms in genes related to clearance, such as the degrading enzyme neprilysin [37, 38], may influence an individual's risk of AD. It is thought that plaques may be cleared by the phagocytic activity of microglia and it is known that Aβ binds specifically to the plasma membranes of both microglia and neurones. On microglia a receptor complex has been identified that mediates the binding to Aβ fibrils [39]. Components of this receptor complex includes the B-class scavenger receptor CD36, the integrin-associated protein/CD47, and the alpha(6)beta(1)-integrin. It has also been reported that the receptor for advanced glycosylation end-products (RAGE) and FPRL1 (formyl peptide receptorlike 1) are able to bind both the monomeric and fibrillar forms of Aβ [40]. Microglia are found around neuritic plaques in the brains of patients with AD and the binding of Aβ to the receptors may stimulate an inflammatory response and mediate peptide clearance. Although these receptors may have a purely beneficial role in delivering peptide to the endosomes for degradation, however in the light of the discussion above, the internalisation of Aβ may in fact result in enhanced aggregation and toxicity.

Aβ AND LONG TERM POTENTIATION

LTP is a phenomenon whereby stimulus-dependent enhancement of synaptic efficacy may encode memories. The role of LTP in the memory deficits of AD has been studied in transgenic mice that express the AD-causing Swedish mutant of human APP. Experiments in brain slices showed loss of LTP in the absence of neuronal death; moreover the loss of LTP correlated with deteriorating performance in behavioural tests of learning [41]. Similar loss of LTP was seen in rat brain slices treated with soluble Aβ aggregates of laboratory-synthesised peptides [42]. Walsh and colleagues have gone on to show that the oligomeric Aβ, secreted from CHO cells expressing a disease-causing APP mutant, can interfere with LTP in intact rat hippocampus. Intracerebroventricular injection of the conditioned medium containing Aβ oligomers was shown to completely abolish LTP, an effect that was not seen when control conditioned medium was injected [43]. Fractionation of Aβ species in the conditioned media into monomers and monomer-free oligomers demonstrated that it was the oligomers that were responsible for the learning deficits in rats following intracerebroventricular injection [44]. The straightforward explanation for the effects on LTP are that extracellular application of Aβ results in an effect mediated at the plasma membrane. However the demonstration of Aβ aggregates in endosomes implies that an intracellular mechanism remains a possibility [43].

Aβ AND NICOTINIC NEUROTRANSMISSION

The disruption of cholinergic neurotransmission occurs early in AD and the elevation of synaptic acetylcholine (ACh) concentrations remains the main therapeutic approach in the clinic. Wang and colleagues have shown that Aβ binds with high affinity to alpha7n Ach receptors [45] resulting in the inhibition of receptor-dependent calcium signalling and acetylcholine release, two processes critically involved in neurotransmission and synaptic plasticity. The binding interaction between exogenous Aβ and the alpha 7 receptor may well facilitate the internalization and intracellular accumulation of Aβ in Alzheimer's disease brains. Indeed intracellular accumulation of Aβ in neurons has been shown in a cell culture model to correlate with the level of this receptor [46] and Aβ internalization can be blocked by alpha-bungarotoxin, an alpha 7 receptor antagonist. Moreover the high levels of the alpha 7 receptor found in the hippocampus and cortex [47] may account for the early involvement of these brain regions in AD. Although nicotinic stimulation has traditionally been seen as beneficial in AD (reviewed by Buccafusco *et al.* [48]) because of improved LTP and reduced amyloid deposition [49, 50] there is concern that up regulation of ACh receptors in smokers [51] may increase the proportion of the total Aβ that is soluble [50] and available for internalisation. This may account for the exacerbation of alpha 7 receptor-mediated tau phosphorylation [52] in transgenic mice treated with nicotine [53].

Aβ AND ELECTRICAL PROPERTIES OF MEMBRANES

The electrical integrity of biological membranes is particularly important for the correct functioning and survival of neurones. Disruption of the resting potential across the plasma membrane may contribute to the toxic effects of Aβ as described in the preceding sections, namely LTP deficits and aberrant neurotransmission. In a similar way, disruption of the mitochondrial membrane may result in the oxidative stress [54] component of AD pathogenesis. There is however conflicting data about how oligomers cause membrane disruption; some groups have shown pore-like Aβ aggregates that insert into membranes;

others have evidence that membrane conductivity is increased but in the absence of discrete ion channel activity [55].

Pore-like aggregates of Aβ have a doughnut-shaped appearance, [56] being composed of 30-60 peptides monomers [2, 57] and resembling pore-forming bacterial toxins. These pore-like aggregates are proposed to insert into membranes forming a pathological ion channel, causing depolarisation of membranes and possibly calcium influx into the cell. In support of this hypothesis Lin and colleagues can demonstrate that pore-like aggregates have discrete ion channel activity that can be inhibited by zinc ions [56].

However, Aβ may share a channel-independent mechanism of membrane disruption with other aggregation-prone proteins. A recent study using fluorescently-loaded SHSY5Y cells showed that application of $Aβ_{1-42}$ and other oligomeric aggregates elevated intracellular Ca^{2+}, an effect that persisted even after depletion of intracellular Ca^{2+} stores [16]. The fact that the potent Ca^{2+} channel blocker cobalt failed to affect this response combined with the rapid leakage of anionic fluorescent dyes, point to a generalized increase in membrane permeability. This study provided evidence that the unregulated flux of ions across "leaky" membranes may provide a common mechanism for oligomer-mediated toxicity in many amyloid diseases. The dysregulation of calcium metabolism is likely to play an important role [58] because of the strong transmembrane concentration gradient and the involvement of calcium in intracellular signalling.

THE ROLE OF OXIDATIVE STRESS

It is well established that oxidative stress, as measured by oxidation products of proteins [59-61], lipids [62-64] and nucleic acids [65-68], has an important role in the pathogenesis of AD. Many of these studies have been performed in clinical specimens from late disease, however recent work has shown that isoprostane levels, a biochemical marker of lipid oxidation, are elevated even at the earliest stages of clinical AD [69].

How the reactive oxygen species are generated is hotly debated, however it is known that Aβ peptides are able to bind copper ions (Cu(II)) and reduce them (to Cu(I)), releasing hydrogen peroxide. Others metals may also be involved in similar reactions with aluminium and iron being possible candidates. Other workers have suggested that mitochondrial membrane disruption may release oxidative species. Interestingly, in concordance with the idea that it is the process of Aβ aggregation that is toxic, Tabner and colleagues have shown that, in the absence of redox-active metal ions, the earliest stages of Aβ aggregation can generate a brief burst of hydrogen peroxide [70].

CONCLUSION

There is an ongoing debate as to how Aβ causes neuronal dysfunction and death. The focus has recently been on small, soluble aggregates of Aβ, as the pathogenic agent however recent work suggest that the process of aggregation may be toxic, perhaps by generating oxidative species. A better understanding of the significance of intracellular Aβ may provide us with new therapeutic strategies for Alzheimer's disease.

REFERENCES

[1]   Nilsberth, C.; Westlind-Danielsson, A.; Eckman, C. B.; Condron, M. M.; Axelman, K.; Forsell, C.; Stenh, C.; Luthman, J.; Teplow, D. B.; Younkin, S. G.; Naslund, J.; Lannfelt, L. The 'Arctic' APP mutation (E693G) causes Alzheimer's disease by enhanced Abeta protofibril formation. *Nat Neurosci* 4: 887-893., 2001.

[2]   Lashuel, H. A.; Hartley, D. M.; Petre, B. M.; Wall, J. S.; Simon, M. N.; Walz, T.; Lansbury, P. T., Jr. Mixtures of wild-type and a pathogenic (E22G) form of Abeta40 in vitro accumulate protofibrils, including amyloid pores. *J Mol Biol* 332: 795-808, 2003.

[3]   Katzman, R.; Terry, R.; DeTeresa, R.; Brown, T.; Davies, P.; Fuld, P.; Renbing, X.; Peck, A. Clinical, pathological, and neurochemical changes in dementia: a subgroup with preserved mental status and numerous neocortical plaques. *Ann Neurol* 23: 138-144, 1988.

[4]   Delaere, P.; Duyckaerts, C.; Masters, C.; Beyreuther, K.; Piette, F.; Hauw, J. J. Large amounts of neocortical beta A4 deposits without neuritic plaques nor tangles in a psychometrically assessed, non-demented person. *Neurosci Lett* 116: 87-93, 1990.

[5]   Dickson, D. W.; Crystal, H. A.; Bevona, C.; Honer, W.; Vincent, I.; Davies, P. Correlations of synaptic and pathological markers with cognition of the elderly. *Neurobiol Aging* 16: 285-298; discussion 298-304, 1995.

[6]   Braak, H.; Braak, E. Morphological criteria for the recognition of Alzheimer's disease and the distribution pattern of cortical changes related to this disorder. *Neurobiol Aging* 15: 355-356; discussion 379-380, 1994.

[7]   Lue, L. F.; Kuo, Y. M.; Roher, A. E.; Brachova, L.; Shen, Y.; Sue, L.; Beach, T.; Kurth, J. H.; Rydel, R. E.; Rogers, J. Soluble amyloid beta peptide concentration as a predictor of synaptic change in Alzheimer's disease. *Am J Pathol* 155: 853-862, 1999.

[8]   McLean, C. A.; Cherny, R. A.; Fraser, F. W.; Fuller, S. J.; Smith, M. J.; Beyreuther, K.; Bush, A. I.; Masters, C. L. Soluble pool of Abeta amyloid as a determinant of severity of neurodegeneration in Alzheimer's disease. *Ann Neurol* 46: 860-866, 1999.

[9]   Naslund, J.; Haroutunian, V.; Mohs, R.; Davis, K. L.; Davies, P.; Greengard, P.; Buxbaum, J. D. Correlation between elevated levels of amyloid beta-peptide in the brain and cognitive decline. *JAMA* 283: 1571-1577, 2000.

[10]   Gong, Y.; Chang, L.; Viola, K. L.; Lacor, P. N.; Lambert, M. P.; Finch, C. E.; Krafft, G. A.; Klein, W. L. Alzheimer's disease-affected brain: presence of oligomeric A beta ligands (ADDLs) suggests a molecular basis for reversible memory loss. *Proc Natl Acad Sci U S A* 100: 10417-10422, 2003.

[11]   Lambert, M. P.; Barlow, A. K.; Chromy, B. A.; Edwards, C.; Freed, R.; Liosatos, M.; Morgan, T. E.; Rozovsky, I.; Trommer, B.; Viola, K. L.; Wals, P.; Zhang, C.; Finch, C. E.; Krafft, G. A.; Klein, W. L. Diffusible, nonfibrillar ligands derived from Abeta1-42 are potent central nervous system neurotoxins. *Proc Natl Acad Sci U S A* 95: 6448-6453., 1998.

[12]   Hartley, D. M.; Walsh, D. M.; Ye, C. P.; Diehl, T.; Vasquez, S.; Vassilev, P. M.; Teplow, D. B.; Selkoe, D. J. Protofibrillar intermediates of amyloid beta-protein induce acute electrophysiological changes and progressive neurotoxicity in cortical neurons. *J Neurosci* 19: 8876-8884, 1999.

[13] Hoshi, M.; Sato, M.; Matsumoto, S.; Noguchi, A.; Yasutake, K.; Yoshida, N.; Sato, K. Spherical aggregates of beta-amyloid (amylospheroid) show high neurotoxicity and activate tau protein kinase I/glycogen synthase kinase-3beta. *Proc Natl Acad Sci U S A* 100: 6370-6375, 2003.

[14] Kayed, R.; Head, E.; Thompson, J. L.; McIntire, T. M.; Milton, S. C.; Cotman, C. W.; Glabe, C. G. Common structure of soluble amyloid oligomers implies common mechanism of pathogenesis. *Science* 300: 486-489, 2003.

[15] Bucciantini, M.; Giannoni, E.; Chiti, F.; Baroni, F.; Formigli, L.; Zurdo, J.; Taddei, N.; Ramponi, G.; Dobson, C. M.; Stefani, M. Inherent toxicity of aggregates implies a common mechanism for protein misfolding diseases. *Nature* 416: 507-511, 2002.

[16] Demuro, A.; Mina, E.; Kayed, R.; Milton, S. C.; Parker, I.; Glabe, C. G. Calcium dysregulation and membrane disruption as a ubiquitous neurotoxic mechanism of soluble amyloid oligomers. *J Biol Chem* 280: 17294-17300, 2005.

[17] Wogulis, M.; Wright, S.; Cunningham, D.; Chilcote, T.; Powell, K.; Rydel, R. E. Nucleation-dependent polymerization is an essential component of amyloid-mediated neuronal cell death. *J Neurosci* 25: 1071-1080, 2005.

[18] Tanaka, M.; Kim, Y. M.; Lee, G.; Junn, E.; Iwatsubo, T.; Mouradian, M. M. Aggresomes formed by alpha-synuclein and synphilin-1 are cytoprotective. *J Biol Chem* 279: 4625-4631, 2004.

[19] Hartmann, T.; Bieger, S. C.; Bruhl, B.; Tienari, P. J.; Ida, N.; Allsop, D.; Roberts, G. W.; Masters, C. L.; Dotti, C. G.; Unsicker, K.; Beyreuther, K. Distinct sites of intracellular production for Alzheimer's disease A beta40/42 amyloid peptides. *Nat Med* 3: 1016-1020, 1997.

[20] Wild-Bode, C.; Yamazaki, T.; Capell, A.; Leimer, U.; Steiner, H.; Ihara, Y.; Haass, C. Intracellular generation and accumulation of amyloid beta-peptide terminating at amino acid 42. *J Biol Chem* 272: 16085-16088, 1997.

[21] Xu, H.; Sweeney, D.; Wang, R.; Thinakaran, G.; Lo, A. C.; Sisodia, S. S.; Greengard, P.; Gandy, S. Generation of Alzheimer beta-amyloid protein in the trans-Golgi network in the apparent absence of vesicle formation. *Proc Natl Acad Sci U S A* 94: 3748-3752, 1997.

[22] Cook, D. G.; Forman, M. S.; Sung, J. C.; Leight, S.; Kolson, D. L.; Iwatsubo, T.; Lee, V. M.; Doms, R. W. Alzheimer's A beta(1-42) is generated in the endoplasmic reticulum/intermediate compartment of NT2N cells. *Nat Med* 3: 1021-1023, 1997.

[23] Skovronsky, D. M.; Doms, R. W.; Lee, V. M. Detection of a novel intraneuronal pool of insoluble amyloid beta protein that accumulates with time in culture. *J Cell Biol* 141: 1031-1039, 1998.

[24] Greenfield, J. P.; Tsai, J.; Gouras, G. K.; Hai, B.; Thinakaran, G.; Checler, F.; Sisodia, S. S.; Greengard, P.; Xu, H. Endoplasmic reticulum and trans-Golgi network generate distinct populations of Alzheimer beta-amyloid peptides. *Proc Natl Acad Sci U S A* 96: 742-747, 1999.

[25] Perez, R. G.; Soriano, S.; Hayes, J. D.; Ostaszewski, B.; Xia, W.; Selkoe, D. J.; Chen, X.; Stokin, G. B.; Koo, E. H. Mutagenesis identifies new signals for beta-amyloid precursor protein endocytosis, turnover, and the generation of secreted fragments, including Abeta42. *J Biol Chem* 274: 18851-18856, 1999.

[26] Huang, T. H.; Yang, D. S.; Plaskos, N. P.; Go, S.; Yip, C. M.; Fraser, P. E.; Chakrabartty, A. Structural studies of soluble oligomers of the Alzheimer beta-amyloid peptide. *J Mol Biol* 297: 73-87, 2000.

[27] Carrotta, R.; Manno, M.; Bulone, D.; Martorana, V.; San Biagio, P. L. Protofibril formation of amyloid beta-protein at low pH via a non-cooperative elongation mechanism. *J Biol Chem* 280: 30001-30008, 2005.

[28] Kawarabayashi, T.; Shoji, M.; Younkin, L. H.; Wen-Lang, L.; Dickson, D. W.; Murakami, T.; Matsubara, E.; Abe, K.; Ashe, K. H.; Younkin, S. G. Dimeric amyloid beta protein rapidly accumulates in lipid rafts followed by apolipoprotein E and phosphorylated tau accumulation in the Tg2576 mouse model of Alzheimer's disease. *J Neurosci* 24: 3801-3809, 2004.

[29] Marchesi, V. T. An alternative interpretation of the amyloid Abeta hypothesis with regard to the pathogenesis of Alzheimer's disease. *Proc Natl Acad Sci U S A* 102: 9093-9098, 2005.

[30] Walsh, D. M.; Tseng, B. P.; Rydel, R. E.; Podlisny, M. B.; Selkoe, D. J. The oligomerization of amyloid beta-protein begins intracellularly in cells derived from human brain. *Biochemistry* 39: 10831-10839, 2000.

[31] Gouras, G. K.; Tsai, J.; Naslund, J.; Vincent, B.; Edgar, M.; Checler, F.; Greenfield, J. P.; Haroutunian, V.; Buxbaum, J. D.; Xu, H.; Greengard, P.; Relkin, N. R. Intraneuronal Abeta42 accumulation in human brain. *Am J Pathol* 156: 15-20, 2000.

[32] D'Andrea, M. R.; Nagele, R. G.; Wang, H. Y.; Peterson, P. A.; Lee, D. H. in *Histopathology* 120-134 (2001).

[33] Oddo, S.; Caccamo, A.; Shepherd, J. D.; Murphy, M. P.; Golde, T. E.; Kayed, R.; Metherate, R.; Mattson, M. P.; Akbari, Y.; LaFerla, F. M. Triple-transgenic model of Alzheimer's disease with plaques and tangles: intracellular Abeta and synaptic dysfunction. *Neuron* 39: 409-421, 2003.

[34] Casas, C.; Sergeant, N.; Itier, J. M.; Blanchard, V.; Wirths, O.; van der Kolk, N.; Vingtdeux, V.; van de Steeg, E.; Ret, G.; Canton, T.; Drobecq, H.; Clark, A.; Bonici, B.; Delacourte, A.; Benavides, J.; Schmitz, C.; Tremp, G.; Bayer, T. A.; Benoit, P.; Pradier, L. Massive CA1/2 neuronal loss with intraneuronal and N-terminal truncated Abeta42 accumulation in a novel Alzheimer transgenic model. *Am J Pathol* 165: 1289-1300, 2004.

[35] Billings, L. M.; Oddo, S.; Green, K. N.; McGaugh, J. L.; Laferla, F. M. Intraneuronal Abeta causes the onset of early Alzheimer's disease-related cognitive deficits in transgenic mice. *Neuron* 45: 675-688, 2005.

[36] Crowther, D. C.; Kinghorn, K. J.; Miranda, E.; Page, R.; Curry, J. A.; Duthie, F. A.; Gubb, D. C.; Lomas, D. A. Intraneuronal Aβ, non-amyloid aggregates and neurodegeneration in a Drosophila model of Alzheimer's disease. *Neuroscience* 132: 123-135, 2005.

[37] Clarimon, J.; Munoz, F. J.; Boada, M.; Tarraga, L.; Sunyer, J.; Bertranpetit, J.; Comas, D. Possible increased risk for Alzheimer's disease associated with neprilysin gene. *J Neural Transm* 110: 651-657, 2003.

[38] Sakai, A.; Ujike, H.; Nakata, K.; Takehisa, Y.; Imamura, T.; Uchida, N.; Kanzaki, A.; Yamamoto, M.; Fujisawa, Y.; Okumura, K.; Kuroda, S. Association of the Neprilysin gene with susceptibility to late-onset Alzheimer's disease. *Dement Geriatr Cogn Disord* 17: 164-169, 2004.

[39] Bamberger, M. E.; Harris, M. E.; McDonald, D. R.; Husemann, J.; Landreth, G. E. A cell surface receptor complex for fibrillar beta-amyloid mediates microglial activation. *J Neurosci* 23: 2665-2674, 2003.

[40] Verdier, Y.; Zarandi, M.; Penke, B. Amyloid beta-peptide interactions with neuronal and glial cell plasma membrane: binding sites and implications for Alzheimer's disease. *J Pept Sci* 10: 229-248, 2004.

[41] Chapman, P. F.; White, G. L.; Jones, M. W.; Cooper-Blacketer, D.; Marshall, V. J.; Irizarry, M.; Younkin, L.; Good, M. A.; Bliss, T. V.; Hyman, B. T.; Younkin, S. G.; Hsiao, K. K. Impaired synaptic plasticity and learning in aged amyloid precursor protein transgenic mice. *Nat Neurosci* 2: 271-276, 1999.

[42] Wang, H. W.; Pasternak, J. F.; Kuo, H.; Ristic, H.; Lambert, M. P.; Chromy, B.; Viola, K. L.; Klein, W. L.; Stine, W. B.; Krafft, G. A.; Trommer, B. L. Soluble oligomers of beta amyloid (1-42) inhibit long-term potentiation but not long-term depression in rat dentate gyrus. *Brain Res* 924: 133-140, 2002.

[43] Walsh, D. M.; Klyubin, I.; Fadeeva, J. V.; Cullen, W. K.; Anwyl, R.; Wolfe, M. S.; Rowan, M. J.; Selkoe, D. J. Naturally secreted oligomers of amyloid beta protein potently inhibit hippocampal long-term potentiation *in vivo*. *Nature* 416: 535-539, 2002.

[44] Cleary, J. P.; Walsh, D. M.; Hofmeister, J. J.; Shankar, G. M.; Kuskowski, M. A.; Selkoe, D. J.; Ashe, K. H. Natural oligomers of the amyloid-beta protein specifically disrupt cognitive function. *Nat Neurosci* 8: 79-84, 2005.

[45] Wang, H. Y.; Lee, D. H.; D'Andrea, M. R.; Peterson, P. A.; Shank, R. P.; Reitz, A. B. beta-Amyloid(1-42) binds to alpha7 nicotinic acetylcholine receptor with high affinity. Implications for Alzheimer's disease pathology. *J Biol Chem* 275: 5626-5632, 2000.

[46] Nagele, R. G.; D'Andrea, M. R.; Anderson, W. J.; Wang, H. Y. Intracellular accumulation of beta-amyloid(1-42) in neurons is facilitated by the alpha 7 nicotinic acetylcholine receptor in Alzheimer's disease. *Neuroscience* 110: 199-211, 2002.

[47] Breese, C. R.; Adams, C.; Logel, J.; Drebing, C.; Rollins, Y.; Barnhart, M.; Sullivan, B.; Demasters, B. K.; Freedman, R.; Leonard, S. Comparison of the regional expression of nicotinic acetylcholine receptor alpha7 mRNA and [125I]-alpha-bungarotoxin binding in human postmortem brain. *J Comp Neurol* 387: 385-398, 1997.

[48] Buccafusco, J. J.; Letchworth, S. R.; Bencherif, M.; Lippiello, P. M. Long-lasting cognitive improvement with nicotinic receptor agonists: mechanisms of pharmacokinetic-pharmacodynamic discordance. *Trends Pharmacol Sci* 26: 352-360, 2005.

[49] Hellstrom-Lindahl, E.; Mousavi, M.; Ravid, R.; Nordberg, A. Reduced levels of Abeta 40 and Abeta 42 in brains of smoking controls and Alzheimer's patients. *Neurobiol Dis* 15: 351-360, 2004.

[50] Nordberg, A.; Hellstrom-Lindahl, E.; Lee, M.; Johnson, M.; Mousavi, M.; Hall, R.; Perry, E.; Bednar, I.; Court, J. Chronic nicotine treatment reduces beta-amyloidosis in the brain of a mouse model of Alzheimer's disease (APPsw). *J Neurochem* 81: 655-658, 2002.

[51] Mousavi, M.; Hellstrom-Lindahl, E.; Guan, Z. Z.; Shan, K. R.; Ravid, R.; Nordberg, A. Protein and mRNA levels of nicotinic receptors in brain of tobacco using controls and patients with Alzheimer's disease. *Neuroscience* 122: 515-520, 2003.

[52] Wang, H. Y.; Li, W.; Benedetti, N. J.; Lee, D. H. Alpha 7 nicotinic acetylcholine receptors mediate beta-amyloid peptide-induced tau protein phosphorylation. *J Biol Chem* 278: 31547-31553, 2003.

[53] Oddo, S.; Caccamo, A.; Green, K. N.; Liang, K.; Tran, L.; Chen, Y.; Leslie, F. M.; LaFerla, F. M. Chronic nicotine administration exacerbates tau pathology in a transgenic model of Alzheimer's disease. *Proc Natl Acad Sci U S A* 102: 3046-3051, 2005.

[54] Abramov, A. Y.; Canevari, L.; Duchen, M. R. Beta-amyloid peptides induce mitochondrial dysfunction and oxidative stress in astrocytes and death of neurons through activation of NADPH oxidase. *J Neurosci* 24: 565-575, 2004.

[55] Kayed, R.; Sokolov, Y.; Edmonds, B.; McIntire, T. M.; Milton, S. C.; Hall, J. E.; Glabe, C. G. Permeabilization of lipid bilayers is a common conformation-dependent activity of soluble amyloid oligomers in protein misfolding diseases. *J Biol Chem* 279: 46363-46366, 2004.

[56] Lin, H.; Bhatia, R.; Lal, R. Amyloid beta protein forms ion channels: implications for Alzheimer's disease pathophysiology. *Faseb J* 15: 2433-2444, 2001.

[57] Lashuel, H. A.; Hartley, D.; Petre, B. M.; Walz, T.; Lansbury, P. T., Jr. Neurodegenerative disease: amyloid pores from pathogenic mutations. *Nature* 418: 291., 2002.

[58] Mattson, M. P.; Cheng, B.; Davis, D.; Bryant, K.; Lieberburg, I.; Rydel, R. E. beta-Amyloid peptides destabilize calcium homeostasis and render human cortical neurons vulnerable to excitotoxicity. *J Neurosci* 12: 376-389, 1992.

[59] Castegna, A.; Aksenov, M.; Thongboonkerd, V.; Klein, J. B.; Pierce, W. M.; Booze, R.; Markesbery, W. R.; Butterfield, D. A. Proteomic identification of oxidatively modified proteins in Alzheimer's disease brain. Part II: dihydropyrimidinase-related protein 2, alpha-enolase and heat shock cognate 71. *J Neurochem* 82: 1524-1532, 2002.

[60] Castegna, A.; Aksenov, M.; Aksenova, M.; Thongboonkerd, V.; Klein, J. B.; Pierce, W. M.; Booze, R.; Markesbery, W. R.; Butterfield, D. A. Proteomic identification of oxidatively modified proteins in Alzheimer's disease brain. Part I: creatine kinase BB, glutamine synthase, and ubiquitin carboxy-terminal hydrolase L-1. *Free Radic Biol Med* 33: 562-571, 2002.

[61] Castegna, A.; Thongboonkerd, V.; Klein, J. B.; Lynn, B.; Markesbery, W. R.; Butterfield, D. A. Proteomic identification of nitrated proteins in Alzheimer's disease brain. *J Neurochem* 85: 1394-1401, 2003.

[62] Markesbery, W. R.; Carney, J. M. Oxidative alterations in Alzheimer's disease. *Brain Pathol* 9: 133-146, 1999.

[63] Keller, J. N.; Mattson, M. P. Roles of lipid peroxidation in modulation of cellular signaling pathways, cell dysfunction, and death in the nervous system. *Rev Neurosci* 9: 105-116, 1998.

[64] Mattson, M. P. Modification of ion homeostasis by lipid peroxidation: roles in neuronal degeneration and adaptive plasticity. *Trends Neurosci* 21: 53-57, 1998.

[65] Gabbita, S. P.; Lovell, M. A.; Markesbery, W. R. Increased nuclear DNA oxidation in the brain in Alzheimer's disease. *J Neurochem* 71: 2034-2040, 1998.

[66] Lovell, M. A.; Gabbita, S. P.; Markesbery, W. R. Increased DNA oxidation and decreased levels of repair products in Alzheimer's disease ventricular CSF. *J Neurochem* 72: 771-776, 1999.

[67] Nunomura, A.; Perry, G.; Pappolla, M. A.; Wade, R.; Hirai, K.; Chiba, S.; Smith, M. A. RNA oxidation is a prominent feature of vulnerable neurons in Alzheimer's disease. *J Neurosci* 19: 1959-1964, 1999.

[68] Wang, J.; Xiong, S.; Xie, C.; Markesbery, W. R.; Lovell, M. A. Increased oxidative damage in nuclear and mitochondrial DNA in Alzheimer's disease. *J Neurochem* 93: 953-962, 2005.

[69] Markesbery, W. R.; Kryscio, R. J.; Lovell, M. A.; Morrow, J. D. Lipid peroxidation is an early event in the brain in amnestic mild cognitive impairment. *Ann Neurol* 58: 730-735, 2005.

[70] Tabner, B. J.; El-Agnaf, O. M.; Turnbull, S.; German, M. J.; Paleologou, K. E.; Hayashi, Y.; Cooper, L. J.; Fullwood, N. J.; Allsop, D. Hydrogen Peroxide Is Generated during the Very Early Stages of Aggregation of the Amyloid Peptides Implicated in Alzheimer Disease and Familial British Dementia. *J Biol Chem* 280: 35789-35792, 2005.

In: Cognitive Sciences at the Leading Edge
Editor: Miao-Kun Sun, pp. 33-47

Chapter 4

BRAIN FUNCTION IN ALTERED STATES OF CONSCIOUSNESS: COMPARISON BETWEEN ALZHEIMER DEMENTIA AND VEGETATIVE STATE

Mélanie Boly, Eric Salmon and Steven Laureys [*]

Neurology Department and Cyclotron Research Centre,
University of Liège, Belgium

ABSTRACT

Disorder of consciousness is not an all-or-none phenomenon but it rather represents a continuum. Alzheimer's disease (AD) is the most common cause of dementia among people aged 65 and older, and patients are frequently unaware of the importance of their cognitive deficits (Derouesne *et al.*, 1999). Vegetative state (VS) is a clinical entity with a complete lack of behavioural signs of awareness, but preserved arousal (ANA Committee on Ethical Affairs, 1993; The Multi-Society Task Force on PVS, 1994). Both clinical entities share a certain level of consciousness alteration, and a certain similarity in brain metabolic impairment. Here, we review differences and similarities in brain function between these two types of disorders of consciousness, as revealed by functional neuroimaging studies.

Keywords: vegetative state – Alzheimer dementia – functional brain imaging – consciousness.

[*] Corresponding author: Steven Laureys, MD, PhD. Cyclotron Research Centre, University of Liège, Sart Tilman B30. 4000 Liège, Belgium. Email: steven.laureys@ulg.ac.be; Phone number : 00324/3662316; Fax number : 00324/3662946

INTRODUCTION

Consciousness is a multifaceted concept that can be divided into two main components: arousal (i.e., wakefulness, or vigilance) and awareness (e.g., awareness of the self and the environment) (Plum and Posner, 1983; Zeman *et al.*, 1997). Arousal is supported by several brainstem neuron populations that directly project to both thalamic and cortical neurons (Steriade *et al.*, 1997). Awareness is thought to be dependent upon the functional integrity of the cerebral cortex and its sub-cortical connections; each of its many parts are located, to some extent, in anatomically defined regions in the brain (Dehaene and Naccache, 2001; Zeman, 2001). Usually, consciousness is assessed in neurologically disabled patients by the presence of voluntary or meaningful behaviours (in contrast to automatic, reflexive reactions) in response to various external stimulations.

"CONSCIOUSNESS" IN AD

AD is clinically characterized by a dementia syndrome. Current criteria for dementia include a deterioration in cognitive functions, sufficient to impair daily living activities, with mood and behaviour disturbances (APA, 1987). Dementia stages may be defined using a Mini-Mental State Examination (MMSE) score range (Folstein *et al.*, 1975). Usually, a mild stage corresponds to a MMSE score greater than 20, dementia is moderate between scores 20 and 12, and the deficit is severe when MMSE value is below 12.

There are different aspects of impaired consciousness in AD. An episodic memory trouble is the most frequent early clinical symptom (Perry and Hodges, 1996; Fleischman and Gabrieli, 1999). Episodic memory refers to personal episodes that can be associated to precise contextual information, concerning time and place for example. AD patients cannot vividly recollect and re-experience a number of episodes of their (recent) life, in which they were however deeply involved. Such an impairment in processing contextual characteristics of an episode that make it unique for a subject corresponds to a decrease of autonoetic consciousness (Wheeler *et al.*, 1997; Levine *et al.*, 1998; Tulving, 2002).

More generally, AD is characterised by a deficit of controlled cognitive processes that require conscious processing of information. Neuropsychological studies have demonstrated that AD patients show impairment in controlled processes during memory and executive tasks, while automatic activities may be more preserved (Fabrigoule *et al.*, 1998). It is frequently observed that AD patients fail to consciously recollect information whereas they provide target memories in implicit conditions. Several neuropsychological data show that AD patients, because of diminished control capacities, base their daily functioning upon automatic processes (Adam *et al.*, 2005). They remain efficient in routine situations, but are not able to face unexpected situations.

Beside cognitive impairment, dementia symptoms include personality change and altered judgment (APA, 1987). Behavioural and psychological impairments are well described in AD (Cummings *et al.*, 1994; Neary *et al.*, 1998). Importantly, there is an early lack of awareness for self-cognitive or self-behavioural difficulties (an anosognosia for deterioration) in the disease (Kalbe *et al.*, 2005b). AD patients may show different degrees of awareness in different domains (e.g., reasoning, memory, affect; Figure 1), and there happens to be a continuum in levels of anosognosia concerning the cognitive or behavioural deficits in the disease. (Damasio, 1994; Salmon *et al.*, 2005a). The level of anosognosia has been related to many clinical variables, and not always to dementia severity (Salmon *et al.*, 2005b).

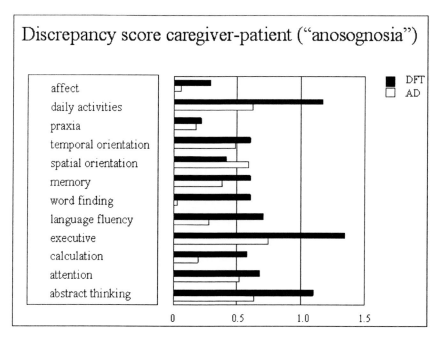

Figure 1. Anosognosia levels in several aspects of cognitive impairment in demented patients, as measured by the discrepancy score between caregivers and patients judgment in Alzheimer disease (AD) and fronto-temporal dementia (DFT)

As dementia develops, patients lose the awareness of time, place and other people (Fishback, 1977). Progression of AD gradually decreases the ability of patients to interact with their environment. Patients may develop aphasia, become unable to recognize friends and family members, and eventually lose the ability to maintain eye contact with their caregivers (Volicer *et al.*, 1987, 1997). As mental oblivion intervenes, the last thing the patient forgets is his/her own name (Fishback, 1977). In later stages, awareness completely disappears, marking the start of a sort of vegetative state (The Multi-Society Task Force on PVS, 1994).

Vegetative State

In 1972, Jennet and Plum defined the vegetative state as a clinical condition of 'wakefulness without awareness'(Jennett and Plum, 1972). These patients have preserved sleep-wake cycles but they do not show clinical signs of awareness of self or environment. They usually present reflex or spontaneous eye opening and breathing, they occasionally move their limbs or trunk in a meaningless way. They may be aroused by painful or prominent stimuli, opening their eyes if they are closed, increasing their respiratory rate, heart rate and blood pressure and occasionally grimacing or moving. Vegetative state patients can make a range of spontaneous movements including chewing, teeth-grinding and swallowing.

More distressingly, they can even show rage, cry, grunt, moan, scream or smile reactions spontaneously or to non-specific stimulation. Their head and eyes sometimes, inconsistently, turn fleeting towards new sounds or sights (Laureys et al., 2000, 2002, 2004). Emergence of vegetative state is defined by the minimally conscious state (MCS). MCS patients show minimal but definite evidence of self or environment awareness but are unable to communicate (Giacino et al., 2002).

Degenerative disorders such as AD are considered as a classical aetiology of vegetative state (The Multi-Society Task Force on PVS, 1994). In patients with degenerative diseases, a persistent vegetative state usually evolves over a period of several months or years (Walshe and Leonard, 1985). Those who remain in a vegetative state may die of superimposed infection or illness. Those who survive such an illness remain in a vegetative state or go into a coma (The Multi-Society Task Force on PVS, 1994). End-of-life questions and ethical debates are similar for VS and bed-ridden, latest stage AD. The question is what action is consistent with the ethical principles of proportionality in balancing the benefits and burdens of medical intervention, and how best to respect the autonomy and self-determination of the patient (Jennett, 1972). It is always difficult to know demented patients' awareness of the end of life. It is also really difficult to accompany these patients, with whom communication is essentially nonverbal (Michel et al., 2002). Many patients with dementia lose the ability to feed themselves in the advanced stages of the disease (McNamara and Kennedy, 2001). Once a patient is considered permanently vegetative, the ethical debate revolves largely around the decision about continuing or withdrawing artificial nutrition and hydration (Jennett, 2005).

GLOBAL CEREBRAL METABOLISM IN VS AND IN AD

Since the beginnings of positron emission tomography (PET) imaging, quantified studies of regional consumption of oxygen and glucose have been performed in AD. They showed a global diminution of cerebral activity (Demetriades, 2002). This diminution of metabolism was proportional to dementia severity (Figure 2; Cutler et al., 1985), being 20% decreased in patients with mild to moderate dementia, and 40% decreased in patients with severe dementia, compared to normal age-matched controls (Frackowiak et al., 1981).

PET has also shown a substantial reduction in global brain metabolism in vegetative patients. Studies of our group and others have shown a 50 to 60% decrease in brain metabolism in vegetative state of different aetiology and duration (Figure 3; Levy et al., 1987; Momose et al., 1989; De Volder et al., 1990; Beuret et al., 1993; Tommasino et al., 1995; Laureys et al., 1999a,b, Rudolf et al., 1999, 2002; Schiff et al., 2002; Edgren et al., 2003). In "permanent" vegetative state (i.e., 12 months after a trauma or 3 months after non-traumatic brain damage), brain metabolism values drop to 30–40% of the normal mean activity (Rudolf et al., 1999, 2002).

A global decrease in cerebral metabolism is not specific to AD or VS. When different anaesthetics are titrated to the point of unresponsiveness, the reduction in brain metabolism is similar to that in comatose patients (Alkire et al., 1995, 1997, 1999). The lowest values of brain metabolism have been reported during propofol anaesthesia (to 28% of the normal range). (Alkire et al., 1995) A transient decrease in brain metabolism also takes place during deep sleep (stage III and IV), (Maquet et al., 1996, 1997, 1999) where cortical cerebral metabolism can drop to nearly 40% of the normal range of values.

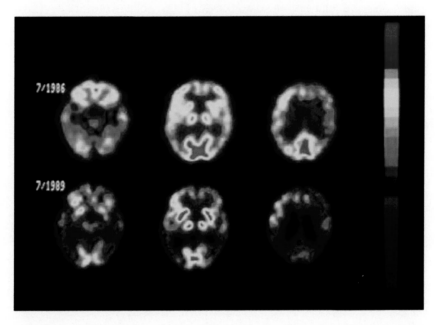

Figure 2. Quantified brain glucose metabolism in a single patient examined twice while in mild dementia stage (1986, upper panel) then in moderate dementia (1989, lower panel). This figure illustrate progressive brain metabolism reduction correlated with the clinical evolution of the Alzheimer disease

Regional Metabolic Distribution

Neuroimaging studies in AD revealed a characteristic regional distribution of decreased activity, showing consistent impairment of metabolism in temporo-parietal cortices, postero-medial regions (posterior cingulate cortex, precuneus), and lateral frontal associative cortices (Salmon, 2002). There is, however, in these patients a relative preservation of primary neo-cortical structures, such as the sensori-motor and primary visual cortex, and also of subcortical structures, like the basal ganglia, brainstem, and thalamus (Herholz et al., 2002). Beside hypometabolism in cortical associative regions, a significant functional impairment of medial temporal regions was also reported in AD (Cutler et al., 1985). However, when voxel-based analysis were used, medial temporal regions were found less diminished than associative cortical regions in these patients (Minoshima et al., 1997). This is even more striking given that brain morphometric studies (voxel-based morphometry) show a major structural temporal medial atrophy (Busatto et al., 2003), and that correlation studies showed a relationship between diminution of amnesic performances and alteration of medial temporal cortex activity (Lekeu et al., 2003). Noteworthy, the involvement of medial temporal structures in autonoetic consciousness remains a matter of debate. It has been suggested that after a stage of diminished hippocampal and entorhinal activity, in the first stages of AD, complexity of medial temporal circuitry would explain local maintenance of activity despite atrophy severity and neurofibrillary histological lesions. One can recognize in AD different 'pathological poles' involving (1) medial posterior regions, often in relationship with frontal and parietal lateral associative regions, or (2) medial temporal regions, but also (3) medial frontal regions, like the anterior cingulate cortex. These poles would be involved variably depending on individuals, and this variability could explain individual clinical profiles (Salmon, 2002).

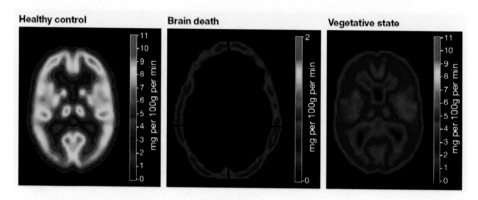

Figure 3. Illustration of the differences in resting brain metabolism measured in brain death and in the vegetative state, compared with controls. The image in patients with brain death shows a clear-cut 'hollow-skull sign', which is tantamount to a 'functional decapitation'. This is markedly different from the situation seen in patients in a vegetative state, in whom cerebral metabolism is massively and globally decreased (to 50% of normal value) but not absent. The colour scale shows the amount of glucose metabolized per 100 g of brain tissue per minute (reproduced with permission from Nature Reviews Neuroscience (Laureys, 2005) copyright 2005 Macmillan Magazines Ltd.)

In AD patients, reduction of metabolism in associative cortical regions is correlated to dementia severity (Salmon et al., 2000, 2005b). This severity is evaluated by means of cognitive capacities scales, like the Mini Mental State Exam or of daily functionality, like the Instrumental Activity of Daily Living scale (Lawton and Brody, 1969). Lower scores mainly reflect lower (consciously) controlled capacities, related to lower metabolism in the first pathological pole just described. Longitudinal PET studies in AD patients showed an expansion as well as an increased severity of hypometabolism in association cortical areas and subcortical structures (Mielke et al., 1996), and a close correlation between progressive metabolic reduction and impaired cognitive performance has been shown (Minoshima et al., 1997; Demetriades, 2002). Some of the fronto-posterior regions included in the first AD pathological pole have been linked, in healthy volunteers, to autonoetic information retrieval, i.e. a remembering with full awareness of re-lived events, which is particularly impaired in AD patients (Whalen and Liberman, 1987).

On the other hand, the metabolic activity of the temporo-parietal junction is in relationship with a measure of anosognosia, i.e. the differential score between a relative and a patient evaluation of cognitive capacities of this patient (Salmon, et al., 2005b). Thus, the anosognosia, or 'decreased of awareness of cognitive impairment' that happens very early in AD reflects a lack of conscious access to daily reality in AD patients, and is related to the activity in a portion of the fronto-posterior associative pathological pole (Kalbe et al., 2005b).

The hallmark of the vegetative state is a complete loss of awareness and a systematic impairment of metabolism in the polymodal associative cortices (bilateral prefrontal regions, Broca's area, parieto-temporal, posterior parietal areas and precuneus and posterior cingulate)

(Laureys *et al.*, 2002). These regions are important in various functions that are necessary for consciousness, such as attention, memory, and language (Baars *et al.*, 2003). On the other hand, VS patients show a relative preservation of metabolism in brainstem, thalamus and posterior hypothalamic regions. In rare cases where patients in a vegetative state recover awareness of self and environment, PET shows a functional recovery of metabolism in these same cortical regions (Laureys *et al.*, 1999b).

The pattern of metabolic impairment in fronto-parietal associative areas found in VS is quite similar to that found in advanced AD (Figure 4). In AD as in VS, the medial posterior cortex has received great attention. The posterior cingulate, retrosplenial cortex and precuneus have all been involved in early stages of AD (Neunzig and Kunze, 1987; Minoshima *et al.*, 1997). In AD, posterior cingulate cortex metabolism is inversely correlated to score reduction in MMSE examination (Figure 5; Salmon *et al.*, 2000). Similarly, the medial parietal cortex (precuneus) and adjacent posterior cingulate cortex seem to be the brain regions that differentiate patients in minimally conscious state from those in vegetative state (Laureys *et al.*, 2004). Interestingly, these areas are among the most active brain regions in conscious waking (Maquet *et al.*, 1996; Gusnard and Raichle, 2001) and are among the least active regions in altered states of consciousness such as halothane (Alkire *et al.*, 1999) or propofol (Fiset *et al.*, 1999) -induced general anaesthesia, sleep (Maquet *et al.*, 1996, 1999), hypnotic state (Maquet *et al.*, 1997; Rainville *et al.*, 1999), and also in Wernicke–Korsakoff's or postanoxic amnesia (Aupee *et al.*, 2001). In a recent study, Vogt et al. suggested that the ventral portion of the posterior cingulate cortex would be related to processing of events for their self/emotional significance (Vogt *et al.*, 2005).

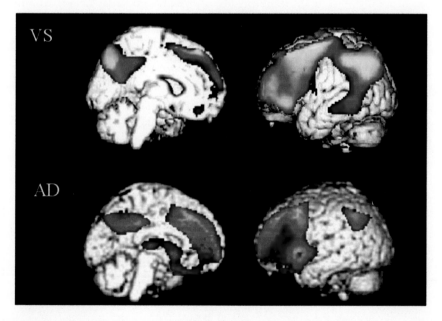

Figure 4. Regional metabolic alteration as compared to healthy subjects in patients in vegetative state (VS, upper panel) and Alzheimer demented patients (AD, lower panel) reveals a striking similarity in medial and lateral fronto-parietal associative areas impairment between both populations

Other PET and fMRI studies showed involvement of precuneus in reflective self-awareness (Kjaer *et al.*, 2002) and processing of one's own name compared to other names

(Vogeley *et al.*, 2004; Perrin *et al.*, 2005). Precuneus and posterior cingulate cortex may thus be part of the neural network subserving human consciousness (Baars *et al.*, 2003), especially of a midline parieto-frontal core involved in self-awareness (Lou *et al.*, 2005).

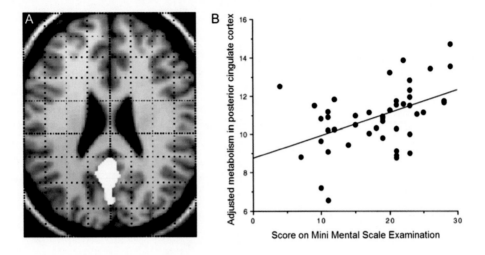

Figure 5. A. Early decrease of activity in posteromedial areas (encompassing posterior cingulate cortex and precuneus) in patients with Alzheimer's disease. B. Linear correlation between dementia severity (score on mini mental state examination) and metabolism in posterior cingulate cortex (area 31, coordinates: x = 0, y =-56, z = 28 mm) in Alzheimer's disease. (From Salmon et al., 2000, reprinted with permission of Wiley-Liss, Inc., a subsidiary of John Wiley and Sons, Inc)

FUNCTIONAL CONNECTIVITY

In AD, some studies showed a functional disconnection between certain pathological poles, i.e. a diminished functional correlation between parahippocampal and frontal regions (Lekeu *et al.*, 2003), or between prefrontal and other associative brain areas involved in short term memory tasks (Grady *et al.*, 2001). EEG studies also showed decreased interhemispheric EEG coherence in AD, reflecting both a lower mean level of functional connectivity as well as diminished fluctuations in the level of synchronization (Stam *et al.*, 2005). Other studies show a decreased complexity of EEG patterns and reduced information transmission among cortical areas in AD (Jeong, 2004). Diffusion tensor magnetic resonance imaging was also used to compare the integrity of several white matter fibre tracts in patients with probable AD (Rose *et al.*, 2004; Bozzali *et al.*, 2002). Relative to normal controls, patients with probable AD showed a highly significant reduction in the integrity of the association white matter fibre tracts, such as the splenium of the corpus callosum, superior longitudinal fasciculus, and cingulum. By contrast, pyramidal tract integrity seemed unchanged (Rose *et al.*, 2000). In another study, strong correlations were found between the mini mental state examination score and the average overall white matter integrity (Bozzali *et al.*, 2002). All these data are in line with the hypothesis that AD is a disconnection pathology, linked to the distribution of histological lesions in the different cortical layers (Knowles *et al.*, 1999). Activation studies in AD have broadly showed two types of patterns. In some memory studies, there is a decrease of activation in pathological poles such as the medial temporal area, probably related to impaired performances in memory tasks. In very early cases, it is however possible to observe a "normal" hippocampal activation, that might be related to compensatory functioning. In most reports, AD patients show activation in more cortical areas than their controls. The hypotheses are (1) that supplementary activation correspond to recruitment of further resources to reach the current performance or (2) that a non-efficient and useless activation occurs because selection and inhibition processes are deficient.

In vivo brain imaging data show multifocal brain atrophy (Juengling et al., 2005) and impaired functional connectivity in patients in VS (Laureys et al., 1999a, 2000). The resumption of long range functional connectivity between different associative cortices (Laureys et al., 2004) and between some of these and the intralaminar thalamic nuclei parallels the restoration of the functional integrity of these patients (Laureys et al., 2000b). An EEG study in a single VS patient showed markedly asymmetrically reduced EEG coherence in relationship with subcortical structural damage (Davey et al., 2000). In cohort studies of patients unambiguously meeting the clinical diagnosis of vegetative state, simple noxious somatosensory (Laureys et al., 2002) and auditory (Laureys et al., 2000a; Boly et al., 2004) stimuli have shown systematic activation of primary sensory cortices and lack of activation in higher order associative cortices from which they were functionally disconnected. High intensity noxious electrical stimulation activated midbrain, contralateral thalamus, and primary somatosensory cortex (Laureys et al., 2002). However, secondary somatosensory, insular, posterior parietal, and anterior cingulate cortices, which were activated in all control individuals, did not show significant activation in any patient. Moreover, in patients in a vegetative state, the activated primary somatosensory cortex was functionally disconnected from higher-order associative cortices of the pain matrix (Laureys et al., 2002). Similarly, although simple auditory stimuli activated bilateral primary auditory cortices, higher-order multimodal association cortices were not activated. A cascade of functional disconnections were also observed along the auditory cortical pathways, from primary auditory areas to multimodal and limbic areas (Laureys et al., 2000a), suggesting that the observed residual cortical processing in the vegetative state does not lead to integrative processes, which are thought to be necessary for awareness. In contrary, functional connectivity analysis for similar simple auditory stimuli, performed in patients in a minimally conscious state, showed preserved functional connections between secondary auditory cortex and a large set of cortical areas (encompassing frontal and temporal association cortices) compared to VS patients (Boly et al., 2004).

CONCLUSION

Disorder of consciousness should be considered as a continuum, not as an all-or-none phenomenon. Our review of correlation and longitudinal studies suggests that this is true in dementia as well as in severely brain injured patients like in vegetative and minimally conscious states. However, progression to VS is rarely present in AD patients (Volicer et al., 1997). Even in the end stage dementia, some behavioural signs of consciousness remain in most cases. Experienced caregivers can detect a discomfort even in patients with very advanced dementia who are unable to maintain their posture in a chair and are mute (Hurley *et al.*, 1992). Late-stage patients are in fact quite different from one another and in most cases continue to interact with their environment (Boller *et al.*, 2002).

Looking at functional imaging data, both patients' populations show diminished global metabolism, diminished regional metabolism in associative areas with a relative preservation of brainstem, thalamus and primary sensory cortices, and impaired functional connectivity. These similarities in brain activity impairment patterns could reflect the general mechanisms of alteration of consciousness present in both clinical conditions, with impairment of the parieto-frontal associative network thought to be necessary to reach conscious perception (global workspace theory (Baars *et al.*, 2003)).

The level of metabolic alteration in the hippocampus and its role in autonoetic consciousness impairment in AD patients remain a matter of debate, even if its structural atrophy was related to episodic memory impairment early in the evolution of AD. Medial temporal regions seem not to be part of the more metabolically impaired regions in VS and were not related to impaired consciousness in this population of patients. A direct comparisons of metabolic disturbances in both conditions might add to the discussion on altered consciousness in neurological diseases and its physiopathological correlations.

ACKNOWLEDGEMENTS

The work in the Cyclotron Research Centre in Liege was made possible by grants from the National Fund for Scientific Research (FNRS), Fondation Medical Reine Elisabeth, a 5th European Framework project (NEST-DD) and InterUniversity Attraction Pole 5/04 – Belgian Science Policy. SL is also supported by FNRS grants 3.4517.04 and by grants from the Centre Hospitalier Universitaire Sart Tilman, the University of Liège, and the Mind Science Foundation. MB and SL are respectively Research Fellow and Research Associate at the Fonds National de la Recherche Scientifique (FNRS).

REFERENCES

Adam, S., Van der Linden, M., Collette, F., Lemauvais, L. and Salmon, E. Further exploration of controlled and automatic memory processes in early Alzheimer's disease. *Neuropsychology* 19: 420-427, 2005.

Alkire, M.T., Haier, R.J., Barker, S.J., Shah, N.K., Wu, J.C. and Kao, Y.J. Cerebral metabolism during propofol anesthesia in humans studied with positron emission tomography. *Anesthesiology* 82: 393-403, 1995.

Alkire, M.T., Haier, R.J., Shah, N.K. and Anderson, C.T. Positron emission tomography study of regional cerebral metabolism in humans during isoflurane anesthesia. *Anesthesiology* 86: 549-557, 1997.

Alkie, M.T., Pomfrett, C.J., Haier, R.J., Gianzero, M.V., Chan, C.M., Jacobsen, B.P. and Fallon, J.H. Functional brain imaging during anesthesia in humans: effects of halothane on global and regional cerebral glucose metabolism. *Anesthesiology* 90: 701-709, 1999.

ANA Committee on Ethical Affairs. Persistent vegetative state: report of the American Neurological Association Committee on Ethical Affairs. *Ann. Neurol.* 33: 386-390, 1993.

APA. *Diagnostic and statistical manual of mental disorders (3d edition revised).* American Psychiatric Association, Washington DC, 1987.

APA (1994) *Diagnostic and statistical manual of mental disorders (4th edition).* American Psychiatric Association, Washington DC, 1987.

Aupee, A.M., Desgranges, B., Eustache, F., Lalevee, C., de la Sayette, V., Viader, F. and Baron, J.C. Voxel-based mapping of brain hypometabolism in permanent amnesia with PET. *Neuroimage* 13: 1164-1173, 2001.

Baars, B.J., Ramsoy, T.Z. and Laureys, S. Brain, conscious experience and the observing self. *Trends Neurosci.* 26: 671-675, 2003.

Beuret, P., Feihl, F., Vogt, P., Perret, A., Romand, J.A. and Perret, C. Cardiac arrest: prognostic factors and outcome at one year. *Resuscitation* 25: 171-179, 1993.

Boller, F., Verny, M., Hugonot-Diener, L. and Saxton, J. Clinical features and assessment of severe dementia. A review. *Eur. J. Neurol.* 9: 125-136, 2002.

Boly, M., Faymonville, M.E., Peigneux, P., Lambermont, B., Damas, P., Del Fiore, G., Degueldre, C., Franck, G., Luxen, A., Lamy, M., Moonen, G., Maquet, P. and Laureys, S. Auditory processing in severely brain injured patients: differences between the minimally conscious state and the persistent vegetative state. *Arch. Neurol.* 61: 233-238, 2004.

Bozzali, M., Falini, A., Franceschi, M., Cercignani, M., Zuffi, M., Scotti, G., Comi, G. and Filippi, M. White matter damage in Alzheimer's disease assessed in vivo using diffusion tensor magnetic resonance imaging. *J. Neurol. Neurosurg. Psychiatry* 72: 742-746, 2002.

Busatto, G.F., Garrido, G.E., Almeida, O.P., Castro, C.C., Camargo, C.H., Cid, C.G., Buchpiguel, C.A., Furuie, S. and Bottino, C.M. A voxel-based morphometry study of temporal lobe gray matter reductions in Alzheimer's disease. *Neurobiol. Aging.* 24: 221-231, 2003.

Cummings, J.L., Mega, M., Gray, K., Rosenberg-Thompson, S., Carusi, D.A. and Gornbein, J. The Neuropsychiatric Inventory: comprehensive assessment of psychopathology in dementia. *Neurology* 44: 2308-2314, 1994.

Cutler, N.R., Haxby, J.V., Duara, R., Grady, C.L., Kay, A.D., Kessler, R.M., Sundaram, M. and Rapoport, S.I. Clinical history, brain metabolism, and neuropsychological function in Alzheimer's disease. *Ann. Neurol.* 18: 298-309, 1985.

Damasio, A.R. *Descartes' error : emotion, reason, and the human brain.* G.P. Putnam, New York, 1994.

Davey, M.P., Victor, J.D. and Schiff, N.D. Power spectra and coherence in the EEG of a vegetative patient with severe asymmetric brain damage. *Clin. Neurophysiol.* 111: 1949-1954, 2000.

De Volder, A.G., Goffinet, A.M., Bol, A., Michel, C., de, B.T. and Laterre, C. Brain glucose metabolism in postanoxic syndrome. Positron emission tomographic study. *Arch. Neurol.* 47: 197-204, 1990.

Dehaene, S. and Naccache, L. Towards a cognitive neuroscience of consciousness: basic evidence and a workspace framework. *Cognition* 79: 1-37, 2001.

Demetriades, A.K. Functional neuroimaging in Alzheimer's type dementia. *J. Neurol. Sci.* 203-204: 247-251, 2002.

Derouesne, C., Lacomblez, L., Thibault, S. and LePoncin, M. Memory complaints in young and elderly subjects. *Int. J. Geriatr. Psychiatry* 14: 291-301, 1999.

Edgren, E., Enblad, P., Grenvik, A., Lilja, A., Valind, S., Wiklund, L., Hedstrand, U., Stjernstrom, H., Persson, L., Ponten, U. and Langstrom, B. Cerebral blood flow and metabolism after cardiopulmonary resuscitation. A pathophysiologic and prognostic positron emission tomography pilot study. *Resuscitation* 57: 161-170, 2003.

Fabrigoule, C., Rouch, I., Taberly, A., Letenneur, L., Commenges, D., Mazaux, J.M., Orgogozo, J.M. and Dartigues, J.F. Cognitive process in preclinical phase of dementia. *Brain* 121 (Pt 1): 135-141, 1998.

Fiset, P., Paus, T., Daloze, T., Plourde, G., Meuret, P., Bonhomme, V., Hajj-Ali, N., Backman, S.B. and Evans, A.C. Brain mechanisms of propofol-induced loss of consciousness in humans: a positron emission tomographic study. *J. Neurosci.* 19: 5506-5513, 1999.

Fishback, D.B. Mental status questionnaire for organic brain syndrome, with a new visual counting test. *J. Am. Geriatr. Soc.* 25: 167-170, 1977.

Fleischman, D.A. and Gabrieli, J. Long-term memory in Alzheimer's disease. *Curr. Opin. Neurobiol.* 9: 240-244, 1999.

Folstein, M.F., Folstein, S.E. and McHugh, P.R. "Mini-mental state". A practical method for grading the cognitive state of patients for the clinician. *J. Psychiatr.* 12: 189-198, 1975.

Frackowiak, R.S., Pozzilli, C., Legg, N.J., Du Boulay, G.H., Marshall, J., Lenzi, G.L. and Jones, T. Regional cerebral oxygen supply and utilization in dementia. A clinical and physiological study with oxygen-15 and positron tomography. *Brain* 104: 753-778, 1981.

Giacino, J.T., Ashwal, S., Childs, N., Cranford, R., Jennett, B., Katz, D.I., Kelly, J.P., Rosenberg, J.H., Whyte, J., Zafonte, R.D. and Zasler, N.D. The minimally conscious state: definition and diagnostic criteria. *Neurology* 58: 349-353, 2002.

Grady, C.L., Furey, M.L., Pietrini, P., Horwitz, B. and Rapoport, S.I. Altered brain functional connectivity and impaired short-term memory in Alzheimer's disease. *Brain* 124: 739-756, 2001.

Gusnard, D.A. and Raichle, M.E. Searching for a baseline: functional imaging and the resting human brain. *Nat. Rev. Neurosci.* 2: 685-694, 2001.

Herholz, K., Salmon, E., Perani, D., Baron, J.C., Holthoff, V., Frolich, L., Schonknecht, P., Ito, K., Mielke, R., Kalbe, E., Zundorf, G., Delbeuck, X., Pelati, O., Anchisi, D., Fazio, F., Kerrouche, N., Desgranges, B., Eustache, F., Beuthien-Baumann, B., Menzel, C., Schroder, J., Kato, T., Arahata, Y., Henze, M. and Heiss, W.D. Discrimination between Alzheimer dementia and controls by automated analysis of multicenter FDG PET. *Neuroimage* 17: 302-316, 2002.

Hurley, A.C., Volicer, B.J., Hanrahan, P.A., Houde, S. and Volicer, L. Assessment of discomfort in advanced Alzheimer patients. *Res. Nurs. Health.* 15: 369-377, 1992.

Jennett, B. Thirty years of the vegetative state: clinical, ethical and legal problems. *Prog. Brain Res.* 150: 537-543, 2005.

Jennett, B. and Plum, F. Persistent vegetative state after brain damage. A syndrome in search of a name. *Lancet* 1: 734-737, 1972.

Jeong, J. EEG dynamics in patients with Alzheimer's disease. *Clin. Neurophysiol.* 115: 1490-1505, 2004.

Juengling, F.D., Kassubek, J., Huppertz, H.J., Krause, T. and Els, T. Separating functional and structural damage in persistent vegetative state using combined voxel-based analysis of 3-D MRI and FDG-PET. *J. Neurol. Sci.* 228: 179-184, 2005.

Kalbe, E., Reinhold, N., Brand, M., Markowitsch, H.J. and Kessler, J. A new test battery to assess aphasic disturbances and associated cognitive dysfunctions -- German normative data on the aphasia check list. *J. Clin. Exp. Neuropsychol.* 27: 779-794, 2005a.

Kalbe, E., Salmon, E., Perani, D., Holthoff, V., Sorbi, S., Elsner, A., Weisenbach, S., Brand, M., Lenz, O., Kessler, J., Luedecke, S., Ortelli, P. and Herholz, K. Anosognosia in very mild Alzheimer's disease but not in mild cognitive impairment. *Dement. Geriatr. Cogn. Disord.* 19: 349-356, 2005b.

Kjaer, T.W., Nowak, M. and Lou, H.C. Reflective self-awareness and conscious states: PET evidence for a common midline parietofrontal core. *Neuroimage* 17: 1080-1086, 2002.

Knowles, R.B., Wyart, C., Buldyrev, S.V., Cruz, L., Urbanc, B., Hasselmo, M.E., Stanley, H.E. and Hyman, B.T. Plaque-induced neurite abnormalities: implications for disruption of neural networks in Alzheimer's disease. *Proc. Natl. Acad. Sci. U S A* 96: 5274-5279, 1999.

Laureys, S. Science and society: death, unconsciousness and the brain. *Nat. Rev. Neurosci.* 6: 899-909, 2005.

Laureys, S., Faymonville, M.E., Degueldre, C., Fiore, G.D., Damas, P., Lambermont, B., Janssens, N., Aerts, J., Franck, G., Luxen, A., Moonen, G., Lamy, M. and Maquet, P. Auditory processing in the vegetative state. *Brain* 123: 1589-1601, 2000a.

Laureys, S., Faymonville, M.E., Luxen, A., Lamy, M., Franck, G. and Maquet, P. Restoration of thalamocortical connectivity after recovery from persistent vegetative state. *Lancet* 355: 1790-1791, 2000b.

Laureys, S., Faymonville, M.E., Peigneux, P., Damas, P., Lambermont, B., Del Fiore, G., Degueldre, C., Aerts, J., Luxen, A., Franck, G., Lamy, M., Moonen, G. and Maquet, P. Cortical processing of noxious somatosensory stimuli in the persistent vegetative state. *Neuroimage* 17: 732-741, 2002.

Laureys, S., Goldman, S., Phillips, C., Van Bogaert, P., Aerts, J., Luxen, A., Franck, G. and Maquet, P. Impaired effective cortical connectivity in vegetative state: preliminary investigation using PET. *Neuroimage* 9: 377-382, 1999a.

Laureys, S., Lemaire, C., Maquet, P., Phillips, C. and Franck, G. Cerebral metabolism during vegetative state and after recovery to consciousness. *J. Neurol. Neurosurg. Psychiatry* 67: 121, 1999b.

Laureys, S., Owen, A.M. and Schiff, N.D. Brain function in coma, vegetative state, and related disorders. *Lancet Neurol.* 3: 537-546, 2004.

Lawton, M.P. and Brody, E.M. Assessment of older people: self-maintaining and instrumental activities of daily living. *Gerontologist* 9: 179-186, 1969.

Lekeu, F., Van der Linden, M., Chicherio, C., Collette, F., Degueldre, C., Franck, G., Moonen, G. and Salmon, E. Brain correlates of performance in a free/cued recall task with semantic encoding in Alzheimer disease. *Alzheimer Dis. Assoc. Disord.* 17: 35-45, 2003.

Levine, B., Black, S.E., Cabeza, R., Sinden, M., McIntosh, A.R., Toth, J.P., Tulving, E. and Stuss, D.T. Episodic memory and the self in a case of isolated retrograde amnesia. *Brain* 121 (Pt 10): 1951-1973, 1998.

Levy, D.E., Sidtis, J.J., Rottenberg, D.A., Jarden, J.O., Strother, S.C., Dhawan, V., Ginos, J.Z., Tramo, M.J., Evans, A.C. and Plum, F. Differences in cerebral blood flow and glucose utilization in vegetative versus locked-in patients. *Ann. Neurol.* 22: 673-682, 1987.

Lou, H.C., Nowak, M. and Kjaer, T.W. The mental self. *Prog. Brain Res.* 150: 197-204, 2005.

Maquet, P., Degueldre, C., Delfiore, G., Aerts, J., Peters, J.M., Luxen, A. and Franck, G. Functional neuroanatomy of human slow wave sleep. *J. Neurosci.* 17: 2807-2812, 1997.

Maquet, P., Faymonville, M.E., Degueldre, C., Delfiore, G., Franck, G., Luxen, A. and Lamy, M. Functional neuroanatomy of hypnotic state. *Biol. Psychiatry* 45: 327-333, 1999.

Maquet, P., Peters, J., Aerts, J., Delfiore, G., Degueldre, C., Luxen, A. and Franck, G. Functional neuroanatomy of human rapid-eye-movement sleep and dreaming. *Nature* 383: 163-166, 1996.

McNamara, E.P. and Kennedy, N.P. Tube feeding patients with advanced dementia: an ethical dilemma. *Proc. Nutr. Soc.* 60: 179-185, 2001.

Michel, J.P., Pautex, S., Zekry, D., Zulian, G. and Gold, G. End-of-life care of persons with dementia. *J. Gerontol. A. Biol. Sci. Med. Sci.* 57: M640-644, 2002.

Mielke, R., Schroder, R., Fink, G.R., Kessler, J., Herholz, K. and Heiss, W.D. Regional cerebral glucose metabolism and postmortem pathology in Alzheimer's disease. *Acta Neuropathol. (Berl.)* 91: 174-179, 1996.

Minoshima, S., Giordani, B., Berent, S., Frey, K.A., Foster, N.L. and Kuhl, D.E. Metabolic reduction in the posterior cingulate cortex in very early Alzheimer's disease. *Ann. Neurol.* 42: 85-94, 1997.

Momose, T., Matsui, T. and Kosaka, N. Effect of cervical spinal cord stimulation (cSCS) on cerebral glucose metabolism and blood flow in a vegetative patient assessed by positron emission tomography (PET) and single photon emission computed tomography (SPECT). *Radiat. Med.* 7: 243-246, 1989.

Neary, D., Snowden, J.S., Gustafson, L., Passant, U., Stuss, D., Black, S., Freedman, M., Kertesz, A., Robert, P.H., Albert, M., Boone, K., Miller, B.L., Cummings, J. and Benson, D.F. Frontotemporal lobar degeneration: a consensus on clinical diagnostic criteria. *Neurology* 51: 1546-1554, 1998.

Neunzig, H.P. and Kunze, K. [Clinical aspects and prognosis following severe craniocerebral trauma]. *Fortschr. Neurol. Psychiatr.* 55: 223-230, 1987.

Perrin, F., Maquet, P., Peigneux, P., Ruby, P., Degueldre, C., Balteau, E., Del Fiore, G., Moonen, G., Luxen, A. and Laureys, S. Neural mechanisms involved in the detection of our first name: a combined ERPs and PET study. *Neuropsychologia* 43: 12-19, 2005.

Perry, R.J. and Hodges, J.R. Spectrum of memory dysfunction in degenerative disease. *Curr. Opin. Neurol.* 9: 281-285, 1996.

Plum, F. and Posner, J.B. *The diagnosis of stupor and coma.* Davis,F.A., Philadelphia, 1983.

Rainville, P., Hofbauer, R.K., Paus, T., Duncan, G.H., Bushnell, M.C. and Price, D.D. Cerebral mechanisms of hypnotic induction and suggestion. *J. Cogn. Neurosci.* 11: 110-125, 1999.

Rose, S.E., Chen, F., Chalk, J.B., Zelaya, F.O., Strugnell, W.E., Benson, M., Semple, J. and Doddrell, D.M. Loss of connectivity in Alzheimer's disease: an evaluation of white matter tract integrity with colour coded MR diffusion tensor imaging. *J. Neurol. Neurosurg. Psychiatry* 69: 528-530, 2000.

Rudolf, J., Ghaemi, M., Haupt, W.F., Szelies, B. and Heiss, W.D. Cerebral glucose metabolism in acute and persistent vegetative state. *J. Neurosurg. Anesthesiol.* 11: 17-24, 1999.

Rudolf, J., Sobesky, J., Ghaemi, M. and Heiss, W.D. The correlation between cerebral glucose metabolism and benzodiazepine receptor density in the acute vegetative state. *Eur. J. Neurol.* 9: 671-677, 2002.

Salmon, E. Functional brain imaging applications to differential diagnosis in the dementias. *Curr. Opin. Neurol.* 15: 439-444, 2002.

Salmon, E., Collette, F., Degueldre, C., Lemaire, C. and Franck, G. Voxel-based analysis of confounding effects of age and dementia severity on cerebral metabolism in Alzheimer's disease. *Hum. Brain Mapp.* 10: 39-48, 2000.

Salmon, E., Ruby, P., Perani, D., Kalbe, E., Laureys, S., Adam, S. and Collette, F. Two aspects of impaired consciousness in Alzheimer's disease. *Prog. Brain Res.* 150: 287-298, 2005a.

Salmon, E., Perani, D., Herholz, K., Marique, P., Kalbe, E., Holthoff, V., Delbeuck, X., Beuthien-Baumann, B., Pelati, O., Lespagnard, S., Collette, F. and Garraux, G. Neural correlates of anosognosia for cognitive impairment in Alzheimer's disease. *Hum Brain Mapp.* in press, 2005b.

Schiff, N.D., Ribary, U., Moreno, D.R., Beattie, B., Kronberg, E., Blasberg, R., Giacino, J., McCagg, C., Fins, J.J., Llinas, R. and Plum, F. Residual cerebral activity and behavioural fragments can remain in the persistently vegetative brain. *Brain* 125: 1210-1234, 2002.

Stam, C.J., Montez, T., Jones, B.F., Rombouts, S.A., van der Made, Y., Pijnenburg, Y.A. and Scheltens, P. Disturbed fluctuations of resting state EEG synchronization in Alzheimer's disease. *Clin. Neurophysiol.* 116: 708-715, 2005.

Steriade, M., Jones, E.G. and McCormick, D. *Thalamus.* Elsevier, Amsterdam ; New York, 1997.

The Multi-Society Task Force on PVS. Medical aspects of the persistent vegetative state (1). *N. Engl. J. Med.* 330: 1499-1508, 1994.

Tommasino, C., Grana, C., Lucignani, G., Torri, G. and Fazio, F. Regional cerebral metabolism of glucose in comatose and vegetative state patients. *J. Neurosurg. Anesthesiol.* 7: 109-116, 1995.

Tulving, E. Episodic memory: from mind to brain. *Annu. Rev. Psychol.* 53: 1-25, 2002.

Vogeley, K., May, M., Ritzl, A., Falkai, P., Zilles, K. and Fink, G.R. Neural correlates of first-person perspective as one constituent of human self-consciousness. *J. Cogn. Neurosci.* 16, 817-827, 2004.

Vogt, B.A., Vogt, L. and Laureys, S. Cytology and functionally correlated circuits of human posterior cingulate areas. *Neuroimage* 29: 452-466, 2005.

Volicer, L., Berman, S.A., Cipolloni, P.B. and Mandell, A. Persistent vegetative state in Alzheimer disease. Does it exist? *Arch. Neurol.* 54: 1382-1384, 1997.

Volicer L, Rheaume Y, et al. Progression of Alzheimer-type dementia in institutionalized patients: a cross-sectional study. *J. Appl. Gerontol.* 6: 83-94, 1987.

Walshe, T.M. and Leonard, C. Persistent vegetative state. Extension of the syndrome to include chronic disorders. *Arch. Neurol.* 42: 1045-1047, 1985.

Whalen, D.H. and Liberman, A.M. Speech perception takes precedence over nonspeech perception. *Science* 237: 169-171, 1987.

Wheeler, M.A., Stuss, D.T. and Tulving, E. Toward a theory of episodic memory: the frontal lobes and autonoetic consciousness. *Psychol. Bull.* 121: 331-354, 1997.

Zeman, A. Consciousness. *Brain* 124: 1263-1289, 2001.

Zeman, A.Z., Grayling, A.C. and Cowey, A. Contemporary theories of consciousness. *J. Neurol. Neurosurg. Psychiatry* 62: 549-552, 1997.

In: Cognitive Sciences at the Leading Edge ISBN: 978-1-60456-051-0
Editor: Miao-Kun Sun, pp. 49-65 © 2008 Nova Science Publishers, Inc.

Chapter 5

CATEGORIZATION OF SPECIES-SPECIFIC VOCALIZATIONS IN THE NON-HUMAN PRIMATE: FEATURES GUIDING BEHAVIORAL DISCRIMINATION AND NEURAL PROCESSING IN THE VENTROLATERAL PREFRONTAL CORTEX

Gordon W. Gifford III[1,2][*] *and Yale E. Cohen*[3,4]
[1]Department of Psychology
[2]Institute for Systems Research
University of Maryland at College Park
College Park, MD 20742
[3]Department of Psychological and Brain Sciences
[4]Center for Cognitive Neuroscience
Dartmouth College
Hanover, NH 03755

ABSTRACT

Communication is one of the fundamental components of both human and non-human animal behavior. Whereas the benefits of language in human evolution are obvious, other communication systems have also evolved to transmit information that is critical for survival. This review focuses on auditory communication signals, specifically species-specific vocalizations, and the underlying neural processes that may support their use in guiding goal-directed behavior. We first highlight the fundamental role that species-specific vocalizations play in the socioecology of several species of non-human

[*] Corresponding author: Gordon W. Gifford III, Ph.D., Department of Psychology, University of Maryland at College Park, College Park, MD 20742, Phone: 301 405 2877, FAX: 301 314 9566, E-mail: ggifford@umd.edu

primates, with a focus on rhesus monkeys (Macaca mulatta). Next, we review the structure and function of auditory cortical processing streams involved in spatial and non-spatial processing. Finally, we discuss the role that the ventrolateral prefrontal cortex may play in the categorization of species-specific vocalizations.

Keywords: Auditory system, categorization, non-human primate, and vocalization

THE BEHAVIORAL RELEVANCE OF SPECIES-SPECIFIC VOCALIZATIONS

The species-specific vocalizations of many primate species, as well as other animals, contain information that can be used by a listener as a source of information about objects, events and the status of peers in their environment (See Hauser, 1997, Chapter 1 for a comprehensive review). The information transmitted by a vocalization can be classified into three classes – "cues", "signs", and "signals" – based on their social use by a caller and how the information transmitted by the vocalization can be used by a listener (Cheney and Seyfarth, 1992; Hauser, 1997).

Cues are directly linked to the phenotype of the call producer, such as body weight and body size (Fitch, 1997). These cues provide a listener with information about the identity (Rendall et al., 1998) and sex (Rendall et al., 2004) of a caller. For example, female macaques use vocal cues to identify different matrilineal relatives (Rendall et al., 1996). In another example, baboons use cues to identify female and male conspecifics (Rendall et al., 2004). This capacity is important since it provides a listener the means to identify individuals with whom they can engage in beneficial social behaviors such as food foraging and social grooming (Rendall et al., 1996) as well as information on individuals they wish to avoid. Finally, since vocal cues are shaped by natural selection (Hauser, 1997) (i.e., a product a caller's physical characteristics), they cannot be readily manipulated and provide a listener with a veridical source of information about a specific caller. A listener's ability to use cues is based on their ability to analyze and determine the harmonic structure of a vocalization (Rendall et al., 1998). Consequently, certain vocalizations provide better information about caller identity than others (Owren and Rendall, 2003). Coos, since they have a clear harmonic structure (Fig. 1A) are useful in caller identification. Grunts (Fig. 1B) or screams, however, are not that useful since these vocalizations are characterized by a more noisy acoustic structure.

The second type of information contained in vocalizations is a "sign". The information contained in signs, unlike cues, is not shaped by natural selection (Hauser, 1997). Instead, the information transmitted by a sign is due to a listener's capacity to associate the acoustic features of a particular call with the status of a caller or the caller's location. One example of a this capacity is the copulation call of the male rhesus macaque (Hauser, 1993). The copulation call provides potential mates with information about the caller's fitness. However, the production of this call can also be used by rival males as a sign of the presence and the location of a mating competitor. As a result, as males increase their production of copulation calls, they not only increase the likelihood of coming into contact with receptive females but also increase the likelihood of encountering aggressive mating competitors (Hauser, 1993). In this way, a listener can use the information contained in vocalizations in behavioral contexts outside the purpose for which it was produced.

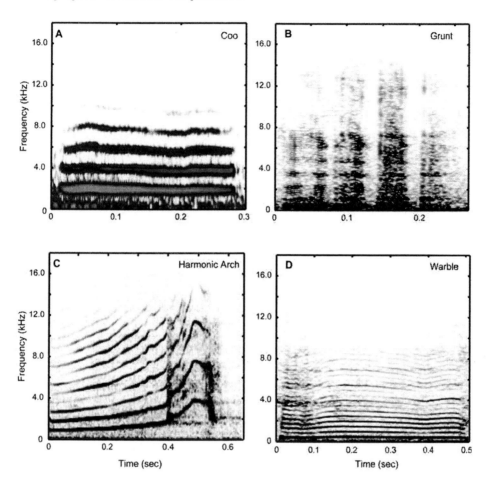

Figure 1: Sound spectrograms of the four call types: (A) coos, (B) grunts, and (C) harmonic arches and (D) warbles. Note that the time scale on the abscissa is different in each panel.

Third, vocalizations can transmit functional (i.e., "referential") information about an event or the presence of an object in the environment. That is, based on signal morphology alone, and regardless of the mechanisms that might underlie vocalization production, listeners are able to extract information about a vocalization's putative meaning. A classic example of referential communication signaling is the predator alarm calls of vervet monkeys (Seyfarth et al., 1980). Vervets produce unique alarm calls for three different predators, a snake, a leopard, and an eagle. The information that is transmitted to the listeners initiates specific patterns of species-specific behaviors. Specifically, when they hear an eagle-alarm call, vervets scan the sky for visual cues of the airborne predator, and in some cases, run to locations that provide overhead coverage. In contrast, when they hear a snake-alarm call, vervets stand up and scan the ground. Finally, a leopard-alarm call initiates a third distinct behavior: vervets run up the nearest tree while scanning the horizon for the presence of a leopard.

The capacity to successfully use referents also allows an animal to use the referent information that is transmitted by another species' vocalizations. For example, female Diana monkeys produce a predator alarm call in response to hearing a leopard-alarm call from conspecific males or the leopard-alarm call of the crested guinea fowl (Zuberbuhler, 2000; Zuberbuhler, 2000; Zuberbuhler and Seyfarth, 1997). Diana monkeys also form mixed species associations with putty-nose monkeys based on the ability of putty-nose monkeys to provide vocal warnings of eagle predation (Eckardt and Zuberbuhler, 2004). These observations suggests that Diana monkeys can form abstract categorical representations of a vocalization's functional meaning that is independent of acoustics and the species generating the signal.

Another example of categorization based on the referent meaning of vocalizations is the behavioral responses of rhesus macaques to food-associated calls (Hauser and Marler, 1993; Hauser and Marler, 1993). In the context of food, wild rhesus produce four acoustically distinct, vocalizations to signal the presence of food items: coos (Fig. 1A), grunts (Fig. 1B), harmonic arches (Fig. 1C), and warbles (Fig. 1D). Warbles and harmonic arches are produced in the presence of rare, high-quality food items (e.g., a piece of coconut). In contrast, in the presence of common, low-quality food items, rhesus produce coos or grunts. These two vocalizations are also produced in the context of positive social interactions, but the acoustic structure of the grunt vocalizations differs from those produced in food contexts (Hauser, 1998; Hauser and Marler, 1993). Analogous to Diana monkeys, wild and laboratory-housed rhesus categorize these food-associated calls based on their referential information and not their acoustic features (Hauser, 1998; Gifford III et al., 2003). That is, rhesus monkeys do not discriminate between call types that transmit the same information about high-quality food (i.e., harmonic arches and warbles), even though these vocalizations have distinct acoustic features. In contrast, rhesus monkeys do discriminate between call types that transmit different referential information (i.e., harmonic arches/warbles and grunts). Taken together, these findings from Diana and rhesus monkeys illustrate how a primate's response to a vocalization can depend more on the functional category that a vocalization represents than its acoustic morphology.

Finally, referential signaling may be formed by combining different vocalizations from multiple species. For example, Diana monkeys, while responding appropriately to the leopard-alarm and eagle-alarm calls of Campbell's monkeys, also respond appropriately to these alarm calls when they are preceded by the Campbell's monkeys' "boom" vocalization that signifies a lower-level threat (Zuberbuhler, 2000). More recent studies suggests that putty-nosed monkeys can also combine referent alarm calls - for leopards and eagles - together to form a new referent that transmits information about group movement, independent of the occurrence of a predator (Arnold and Zuberbuhler, 2006).

NEURAL PATHWAYS INVOLVED
IN VOCALIZATION PROCESSING

Many, if not most, recent investigations into the neural basis of vocalization processing in awake and behaving non-human primates have focused on processing in the temporal lobe (Barbour and Wang, 2003; Bendor and Wang, 2005; Kadia and Wang, 2003; Lu et al., 2001; Lu and Wang, 2004; Wang et al., 2003). These studies have highlighted many important features that relate to vocalization processing. For example, neurons in the primary auditory cortex and regions of the belt and parabelt of marmosets code the temporal features found in vocalizations (Lu et al., 2001; Lu and Wang, 2004; Wang et al., 2003). Also, many neurons in the primate auditory cortex and the surrounding belt and parabelt areas of the marmoset are sensitive to spectral contrast (Barbour and Wang, 2003) and the pitch (Bendor and Wang, 2005) of an auditory stimulus, which may be used to infer the affective content of a vocalization (Bendor and Wang, 2005) .

While insights into how the auditory system represents the acoustic and perceptual features of stimuli are critical for understanding vocalization processing, this level of investigation can not fully explain how the auditory system represents the of more abstract qualities of a vocalization that are used to guide behavior (Wang, 2000; Wang and Kadia, 2001; see Wang, 2000 for a comprehensive review). How is the affective quality of a vocalization represented beyond the neural coding of percepts like pitch? Does the auditory system represent the referent information that is transmitted by a vocalization separate from its acoustic properties? To address these questions we have begun a series of experiments that test how the more abstract qualities of vocalizations are represented in areas outside of the temporal lobe.

Prior to discussing these experiments and to put them into some context, we review an important model of auditory, as well as visual, function. This model posits that the spatial and non-spatial processing of auditory stimuli occurs in parallel (i.e., independent) pathways: a "dorsal" pathway that preferentially processes the spatial attributes of a stimulus (*where* is the sound?), and a "ventral" pathway that preferentially processes the non-spatial attributes (*what* is the sound?).

The two proposed pathways for auditory spatial and non-spatial processing originate in the auditory cortex (Divac et al., 1977; Hackett et al., 2001; Hackett et al., 1998; Hackett et al., 1998; Hackett et al., 1999; Hyvärinen, 1982; Kaas and Hackett, 1998; Kaas and Hackett, 1999; Pandya and Kuypers, 1969; Pandya and Yeterian, 1985; Poremba et al., 2003; Romanski et al., 1999; Romanski et al., 1999). In the auditory cortex, there are three anatomically defined areas - the core, belt, and parabelt. Subdivisions within the belt and parabelt form the bases of the spatial and non-spatial pathways. The auditory spatial pathway is defined by a series of projections that originate in the caudal belt and includes the posterior parietal cortex (particularly, the lateral intraparietal area [area LIP]) and the dorsolateral prefrontal cortex (i.e., the frontal eye fields; area 8a); auditory input to area LIP may also be due to input from multimodal cortical areas and the frontal eye fields (Baizer et al., 1991; Blatt et al., 1990; Schall et al., 1995; Seltzer and Pandya, 1991). In contrast, the auditory non-spatial pathway is defined by a series of projections that originate in the anterior belt and includes regions of the prefrontal cortex.

This parcelization of auditory function is not unique to non-human primates. In humans, there are several lines of anatomical (Galaburda and Sanides, 1980; Rivier and Clarke, 1997; Tardif and Clarke, 2001), neurophysiological (Alain et al., 2001; Anourova et al., 2001; Hart et al., 2004; Maeder et al., 2001; Rämä et al., 2004; Warren and Griffiths, 2003; Warren et al., 2002), and neuropsychological (Clarke et al., 2000) evidence suggesting that distinct pathways process different attributes of an auditory stimulus (Warren and Griffiths, 2003). A "posterior" pathway that includes regions of inferior parietal lobule is thought to process the spatial attributes of an auditory stimulus (Alain et al., 2001; Baumgart et al., 1999; Bremmer et al., 2001; Bremmer et al., 2001; Bushara et al., 2003; Bushara et al., 1999; Cusack et al., 2000; Deouell et al., 2000; Deouell and Soroker, 2000; Griffiths et al., 1998; Hart et al., 2004;

Maeder et al., 2001; Warren et al., 2002). An "anterior" pathway is thought to process the non-spatial attributes of auditory stimuli (Griffiths et al., 1998; Hart et al., 2004; Maeder et al., 2001; Patterson et al., 2002; Scott et al., 2000; Vouloumanos et al., 2001; Zatorre et al., 1992). The areas of the auditory cortex, parietal cortex, and prefrontal cortex that constitute these two pathways may be analogous to those areas identified as important for spatial and non-spatial processing in rhesus monkeys (Rauschecker and Tian, 2000; Romanski et al., 1999).

Whereas this auditory parallel-processing scheme is conceptually elegant and forms an important hypothetical framework for neural function (Milner and Goodale, 1995), it has come under serious scrutiny. First, it is not clear whether the parcelization of auditory information into "what" and "where" streams is appropriate (Cohen and Wessinger, 1999; Griffiths et al., 2004; Middlebrooks 2002; Recanzone 2002; Warren et al., 2005; Zatorre et al., 2002). For instance, it has been suggested that these auditory pathways do not code the what/where attributes of an auditory stimulus but, instead, code sound identification (i.e., "what") and coding changes in frequency over time (i.e., "how") (Belin and Zatorre, 2000). It has also been observed that the anatomical connections terminating in multiple sites throughout the prefrontal cortex more likely represent multiple functional pathways that are not strictly parallel (Kaas and Hackett, 1999).

Second, data from our group suggest that even if the parcelization of auditory processing into "what" and "where" is appropriate, these pathways are not strictly parallel: LIP neurons and neurons in the ventrolateral prefrontal cortex (vPFC), an area that is at the apex of the non-spatial pathway, are modulated robustly, if not equally well, by both the spatial and non-spatial attributes of an auditory stimulus (Cohen et al., 2004; Gifford III, and Cohen, 2005). Figure 2 illustrates this degree of spatial and non-spatial modulation for a two vPFC neurons. Figure 2A shows a vPFC neuron that was modulated preferentially by a coo exemplar. However, the firing rate was also modulated by the location from which the coo exemplar is presented. Its firing rate was highest when the coo was presented at the more eccentric contralateral or ipsilateral locations. Figure 2B shows a neuron with a somewhat different response profile. This neuron was modulated primarily by auditory-stimulus location but also somewhat by auditory-stimulus type. For all seven vocalization exemplars, the neuron's firing rate increased as the exemplars were presented at more contralateral locations. The sensitivity to auditory-stimulus type can be seen when comparing the stimulus-period firing rates elicited by the copulation scream, the girney, and the grunt: the stimulus-period firing rate of the neuron was highest when the copulation scream was presented and lowest when the girney or grunt was presented. These two examples are representative of neural responses to both the identity and location of a sound throughout the vPFC. Importantly, similar evidence for such functional convergence can also be found in the visual system (Ferrera et al., 1992; Ferrera et al., 1994; Rizzuto et al., 2005; Sereno and Maunsell, 1998; Toth and Assad, 2002). In both the visual and auditory system, this convergence is most likely mediated by the anatomical connections that exist between the two spatial and non-spatial pathways (Kaas and Hackett, 1999; Kaas and Hackett, 2000; Sereno and Maunsell, 1998; Webster et al., 1994).

What purpose does spatial information serve in the non-spatial pathway? Similarly, what purpose does non-spatial information serve in the spatial pathway? The answers to these questions are not known, but one interesting hypothesis is that the mixture of spatial and non-spatial information may benefit those computations that create consistent perceptual representations that guide goal-directed behavior (Ferrera et al., 1994; Graziano et al., 1997; Kusunoki et al., 2000; Rao et al., 1997; Toth and Assad, 2002).

Despite the functional interactions between these spatial and non-spatial pathways, we hypothesize for several reasons that vPFC neurons might be involved in preferentially processing the functional meaning (i.e., referent) of a vocalization, as opposed to acoustic structures. First, as noted above, the vPFC is thought to be at the apex of a pathway involved in processing auditory objects (Rauschecker and Tian, 2000; Romanski et al., 1999; Romanski et al., 2000). In addition, the vPFC is thought to play an important role in contextually-dependent vocalization production (Jurgens, 2002). Data from the human literature also suggests a role of the vPFC in processing the functional meaning of vocalizations. For instance, Bunge et al. (2003) suggests that the vPFC is involved in the maintenance and retrieval of abstract rules and Gabrieli et al. (1998) posits a role for this region in semantic processing and syntactic working memory.

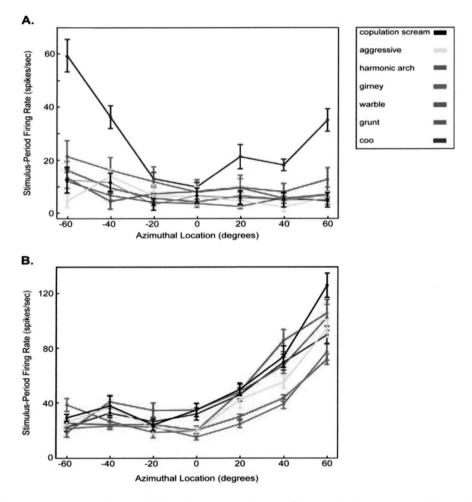

Figure 2: Responses of two vPFC neurons to species-specific vocalizations presented from different azimuthal locations. In both A and B, the mean stimulus-period firing rate of a vPFC neuron is plotted as a function of auditory-stimulus type (colored lines) and auditory-stimulus location (x-axis). The error bars in the panel represent SEM. Negative azimuthal locations are ipsilateral to the recording site, and positive values are contralateral.

THE CATEGORIZATION OF SPECIES-SPECIFIC VOCALIZATIONS IN vPFC

To test the hypothesis that vPFC neurons were preferentially modulated by the referential information that is transmitted by a vocalization (i.e., a vocalization's membership in a functional category), we utilized a paradigm that is relatively unique. vPFC activity was recorded while monkeys listened passively to repeated presentations of one vocalization (the "repeated" vocalization) that was interrupted randomly by the presentation of a second, different ("oddball") vocalization; this type of paradigm is analogous to human studies that test how event-related potentials are modulated by rare ("oddball") stimuli (Näätänen, 1992). We used this paradigm because we were interested in testing the neural mechanisms underlying the "spontaneous" categorization of natural (i.e., ethological) stimuli and not the neural mechanisms that may arise following training with artificial categories (Logothetis and Pauls, 1995; Miller et al., 2002).

Consistent with our hypothesis, we found that vPFC neurons were modulated preferentially by oddball stimuli that were preceded by repetitions of a stimulus that belonged to a different functional category. In contrast, vPFC activity was not modulated preferentially by oddball stimuli that belonged to the same category as the repeated stimulus, even if the oddball and repeated stimuli belonged to different acoustic classes; a vocalization's membership in an acoustic class is based on its acoustic features. These two observations are seen in more detail in Figure 3. In this figure, we plot the normalized population responses of vPFC neurons to the oddball stimuli when it was presented during the (oddball) paradigm described above and during a second paradigm, a "baseline" paradigm. In the baseline paradigm, monkeys listened passively while we presented a variety of auditory stimuli (including the repeated and oddball vocalizations) in a random order with equal probability. When the oddball and repeated vocalizations transmitted different types of referential information (e.g., one was a grunt [low-quality food] and the other was a harmonic arch [high-quality food]) and belonged to different acoustic classes, the average response of vPFC neurons to the oddball vocalization was significantly higher during the oddball paradigm than the response to the same vocalization presented during the baseline condition (Figs. 3Aa and 3Ab). In contrast, when the oddball and repeated vocalizations belonged to different acoustic classes but transmitted the same type of information (i.e., the harmonic arch and warble belong to different acoustic classes but both vocalizations transmit information about high-quality food), the average response of vPFC neurons to the oddball vocalization was not reliably different than its response in the baseline paradigm (Figs. 3Ba and 3Bb). Finally, when the oddball and repeated vocalizations belonged to the same acoustic class, and hence the same functional category (e.g., both are grunts), the average vPFC response to the oddball vocalization was not reliably different than its response to the same vocalization in the baseline condition (Figs. 3Ca-c).

In a second, related study, we tested further the categorical nature of vPFC activity by directly examining spontaneous neural modulation as a function of a vocalizations category membership (Cohen et al., In Press). In this experiment vPFC neural responses to food calls (i.e., both high-quality and low-quality food) and calls associated with various non-food events were collected. Consistent with categorical processing, we found that the vPFC neurons responded differently to vocalizations that transmitted unrelated types of information and similarly to vocalizations that came from the same category.

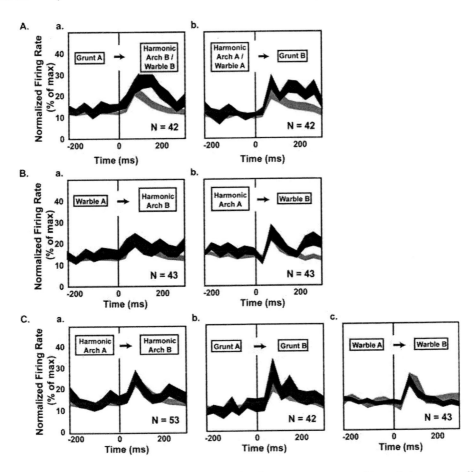

Figure 3: Population responses of vPFC activity in response to transitions between vocalization exemplars. A. Normalized vPFC population activity to a test vocalization that belongs to a different acoustic class and different functional category than the repeated vocalization. B. Normalized vPFC population activity to a test vocalization that belongs to a different acoustic class but the same functional category as the repeated vocalization. C. Normalized vPFC population activity to a test vocalization that belongs to the same acoustic class as the repeated vocalization. The thick grey line in each panel represents the normalized population firing rates in response to a test vocalization during the repetitive-presentation context. The thick black line in each panel represents normalized population firing rates in response to a test vocalization during the random-presentation context. The thickness of the lines indicates activity ranging two standard deviations from the mean response for the population. All data are aligned relative to onset of the test vocalization; the vertical black line indicates stimulus onset. In each panel's schematic, the repeated and test vocalizations for the data are respectively denoted to the left and right of the vertical black line indicating stimulus onset.

However, unlike the results of the previous oddball study, the responses of vPFC neurons did not differentiate between the information transmitted by vocalizations regarding food quality. Specifically, vPFC neural modulation within the categories of low-quality food and high-quality food was not statistically different than vPFC neural modulation between the two categories. These observations are consistent with the hypothesis that vPFC neurons respond to food and non-food vocalizations based on category membership but do not differentiate between categories of food quality. These results contrast with those of our other study, which suggested that in the context of the oddball paradigm vPFC neural responses are modulated by the categorical membership of the non-oddball and oddball food vocalizations (i.e., food quality).

These somewhat different findings may highlight an important issue of experimental design that should be the focus of future study. Specifically, both studies confirm the hypothesis that vPFC responses are modulated by the categorical membership of vocalizations irrespective of their acoustics. However, the context in which vocalizations are presented (i.e., spontaneous responses versus oddball auditory responses) may alter how categorical boundaries are represented in vPFC activity.

Together, these two sets of experimental data are consistent with the proposition that the vPFC may be involved in the computations underlying the spontaneous categorization of natural categories that are based on the referent information transmitted by vocalizations, a key component of auditory-object processing, and not simple acoustic-feature extraction. What role do these categorical representations play in rhesus behavior? One possibility is that the vPFC is part of a circuit involved in the categorization of socially meaningful signals. Indeed, previous work has suggested that vPFC activity may reflect abstract rule-based processes associated with classifying vocal signals (Deacon, 1992; Jürgens, 2002). For instance, the vPFC might contribute to the production of "purposeful" vocalizations or perhaps to the contextually-dependent inhibition of vocalization production.

CONCLUSION

The results of our behavioral work in laboratory-bred macaques illustrate how rhesus macaques respond to "higher-order" features of vocalizations that are not directly related to their acoustic properties. In turn, we have also provided examples of how vPFC neurons at the apex of a hypothesized auditory-object processing stream responds to both the "higher-order" features of a sound and to a lesser extent the spatial attributes of a sound source. The core issue of these studies has been an attempt to understand how the auditory system spontaneously categorizes vocalizations and the potential role that the vPFC may play in that process. Overall, our findings are in line with previous work from Freedman and colleagues (Freedman et al., 2001; Freedman et al., 2002) who demonstrated that PFC neurons are involved in the categorical representation of visual objects.

It is important to note that not all vPFC studies are suggestive of a role of the vPFC in categorization. For instance, a recent study indicated that vPFC activity more closely correlates with the perceptual features of species-specific vocalizations rather than the transmitted information (Romanski et al., 2005). However, our studies and the Romanski et al. study are consistent with the hypothesis that the vPFC is not involved in simple-feature extraction but instead plays an important role in the computations underlying the perception of auditory objects. Thus, it may be that the results of these studies differ only in the nature and extent of these computations and that these differences may be due to differences in recording locations and/or analysis techniques.

One limitation of our studies is the reliance on the "natural" categories associated with specific call types. While these experiments have provided an insight into vPFC's role in the categorization of vocalizations, further experiments are necessary to fully understand the operation of this process and a more general role that it may play in the categorization of conditioned stimuli. To this end, operant training will be necessary to specify the acoustic boundaries along which categories are defined. Operant training will also allow a broader set of acoustic features to be associated with a specific behavioral salience and the creation of novel stimuli that cross perceptual boundaries (Specht et al., 2005). In addition, the flexibility provided by operant training in assigning a categorical salience to a sound would also allow for the examination of how categories are formed and adjusted through experience or context. Finally, the use of this method will provide a greater understanding into whether the mechanisms of spontaneous categorization are fundamentally different from the mechanisms that mediate operantly defined categories (Freedman et al., 2002) and whether categorical representations are dependent on task demand (Freedman et al., 2005).

Beyond the relationship between how the vPFC codes natural and artificial categories, our studies raise several other intriguing and important questions. For example, since communication is often multimodal (Hauser, M. D 1993; Hinde and Rowell, 1962; Partan and Marler, 1999) and since vPFC neurons respond to visual stimuli (Romanski and Goldman-Rakic, 2002), an interesting question to consider is whether this circuit represents auditory as well as visual communication signals and represents this information in a modality-independent format (Ghazanfar and Logothetis, 2003). Also, we do not know whether these categorical representations are formed in the vPFC or just stored there during online processing (Bunge et al., 2003). To address this question, it will be important to test the categorical nature of auditory activity in areas that project to the vPFC (Hackett et al., 1999; Romanski et al., 1999; Romanski et al., 1997; Romanski et al., 1999). Finally, in order to understand how socially meaningful stimuli relate to and promote an animal's behavior, we need to understand how these stimuli are represented and coded across different cortical areas and the role that different areas play in representing different types of referential, affective, and conceptual information. This goal can be accomplished through a systems-level, circuit approach in which neural activity in multiple cortical areas (such as other regions of the PFC, limbic and paralimbic structures, and higher-order visual areas) is targeted to examine their role in the processing information that is critically related to animal's behavior (Barsalou, 1999; Gil-da-Costa et al., 2004; Martin and Chao, 2001; Miller, 2000; Warrington and Shallice, 1984).

ACKNOWLEDGEMENTS

We thank M. LaFleur and B. Russ for their helpful discussions and comments in the preparation of this manuscript. YEC was supported by grants from the Whitehall Foundations, NIH and a Burke Award. GWG was supported by a Ruth L. Kirschstein National Research Service Award research training grant, provided through the Center for Comparative and Evolutionary Biology of Hearing at the University of Maryland at College Park (T32-DC000046 NIDCD).

REFERENCES

Alain, C., Arnott, S. R., Hevenor, S., Graham, S. and Grady, C. L. "What" and "where" in the human auditory system. *Proc Natl Acad Sci U S A* 98: 12301-6, 2001.

Anourova, I., Nikouline, V. V., Ilmoniemi, R. J., Hotta, J., Aronen, H. J. and Carlson, S. Evidence for dissociation of spatial and nonspatial auditory information processing. *Neuroimage* 14: 1268-1277, 2001.

Arnold, K. and Zuberbuhler, K. Language evolution: semantic combinations in primate calls. *Nature* 441: 303, 2006.

Baizer, J. S., Ungerleider, L. G. and Desimone, R. Organization of visual inputs to the inferior temporal and posterior parietal cortex in macaques. *J Neurosci* 11: 168-90, 1991.

Barbour, D. L. and Wang, X. Contrast tuning in auditory cortex. *Science* 299: 1073-5, 2003.

Barsalou, L. W. Perceptual symbol systems. *Behav Brain Sci* 22: 577-609; discussion 610-60, 1999.

Baumgart, F., Gaschler-Markefski, B., Woldorff, M. G. and Scheich, H. A movement-sensitive area in auditory cortex. *Nature* 400: 724-725, 1999.

Belin, P. and Zatorre, R. J. 'What,' 'where' and 'how' in auditory cortex. *Nat Neurosci* 3: 965-966, 2000.

Bendor, D. and Wang, X. The neuronal representation of pitch in primate auditory cortex. *Nature* 436: 1161-5, 2005.

Blatt, G. J., Andersen, R. A. and Stoner, G. R. Visual receptive field organization and cortico-cortical connections of the lateral intraparietal area (area LIP) in the macaque. *J Comp Neurol* 299: 421-45, 1990.

Bremmer, F., Schlack, A., Duhamel, J. R., Graf, W. and Fink, G. R. Space coding in primate posterior parietal cortex. *Neuroimage* 14: S46-51, 2001.

Bremmer, F., Schlack, A., Jon Shah, N., Zafiris, O., Kubischik, M., Hoffman, K.-P., Zilles, K. and Fink, G. R. Polymodal motion processing in posterior parietal and premotor cortex: A human fMRI study strongly implies equivalencies between humans and monkeys. *Neuron* 29: 287-296, 2001.

Bunge, S. A., Kahn, I., Wallis, J. D., Miller, E. K. and Wagner, A. D. Neural circuits subserving the retrieval and maintenance of abstract rules. *J Neurophysiol* 90: 3419-28, 2003.

Bushara, K. O., Hanakawa, T., Immisch, I., Toma, K., Kansaku, K. and Hallett, M. Neural correlates of cross-modal binding. *Nat Neurosci* 6: 190-5, 2003.

Bushara, K. O., Weeks, R. A., Ishii, K., Catalan, M. J., Tian, B., Rauschecker, J. P. and Hallett, M. Modality-specific frontal and parietal areas for auditory and visual spatial localization in humans. *Nat Neurosci* 2: 759-66, 1999.

Cheney, D. L. and Seyfarth, R. M. in *Topics in Primartology, Vol 1: Human Origins* (eds. T. Nishida, W. C. McGrew, P. Marler, M. Pickford and F. de Waal) 315-330 (Tokyo University Press, Tokyo, 1992).

Clarke, S., Bellmann, A., Meuli, R. A., Assal, G. and Steck, A. J. Auditory agnosia and auditory spatial deficits following left hemispheric lesions: evidence for distinct processing pathways. *Neuropsychologia* 38: 797-807, 2000.

Cohen, Y., Hauser, M. and Russ, B. Spontaneous processing of abstract categorical information in the ventrolateral prefrontal cortex. *Biology Letters.*, (In Press).

Cohen, Y. E., Russ, B. E., Gifford III, G. W., Kiringoda, R. and MacLean, K. A. Selectivity for the spatial and nonspatial attributes of auditory stimuli in the ventrolateral prefrontal cortex. *J Neurosci* 24: 11307-16, 2004.

Cohen, Y. E. and Wessinger, C. M. Who goes there? *Neuron* 24: 769-71, 1999.

Cusack, R., Carlyon, R. P. and Robertson, I. H. Neglect between but not within auditory objects. *J Cogn Neurosci* 12: 1056-65, 2000.

Deacon, T. W. Cortical connections of the inferior arcuate sulcus cortex in the macaque brain. *Brain Res* 573: 8-26, 1992.

Deouell, L. Y., Hamalainen, H. and Bentin, S. Unilateral neglect after right-hemisphere damage: contributions from event-related potentials. *Audiol Neurootol* 5: 225-34., 2000.

Deouell, L. Y. and Soroker, N. What is extinguished in auditory extinction? *Neuroreport*: 3059-3062, 2000.

Divac, I., Lavail, J. H., Rakic, P. and Winston, K. R. Heterogenous afferents to the inferior parietal lobule of the rhesus monkey revealed by the retrograde transport method. *Brain Res*: 197-201, 1977.

Eckardt, W. and Zuberbuhler, K. Cooperation and competition in two forest monkeys. *Behavioral Ecology* 15: 400-411, 2004.

Ferrera, V. P., Nealey, T. A. and Maunsell, J. H. Mixed parvocellular and magnocellular geniculate signals in visual area V4. *Nature* 358: 756-761, 1992.

Ferrera, V. P., Rudolph, K. K. and Maunsell, J. H. Responses of neurons in the parietal and temporal visual pathways during a motion task. *Journal of Neuroscience* 14: 6171-86, 1994.

Fitch, W. T. Vocal tract length and formant frequency dispersion correlate with body size in rhesus macaques. *J Acoust Soc Am* 102: 1213-22, 1997.

Freedman, D. J., Riesenhuber, M., Poggio, T. and Miller, E. K. Categorical representation of visual stimuli in the primate prefrontal cortex. *Science* 291: 312-6, 2001.

Freedman, D. J., Riesenhuber, M., Poggio, T. and Miller, E. K. Visual categorization and the primate prefrontal cortex: Neurophysiology and behavior. *J Neurophysiol* 88: 929-941, 2002.

Freedman, D. J., Riesenhuber, M., Poggio, T. and Miller, E. K. Visual categorization and the primate prefrontal cortex: neurophysiology and behavior. *J Neurophysiol* 88: 929-41, 2002.

Freedman, D. J., Riesenhuber, M., Poggio, T. and Miller, E. K. Experience-Dependent Sharpening of Visual Shape Selectivity in Inferior Temporal Cortex. *Cereb Cortex*, 2005.

Galaburda, A. and Sanides, F. Cytoarchitectonic organization of the human auditory cortex. *J Comp Neurol* 190: 597-610, 1980.

Ghazanfar, A. A. and Logothetis, N. K. Neuroperception: facial expressions linked to monkey calls. *Nature* 424: 937-8, 2003.

Gifford III, G. W. and Cohen, Y. E. Spatial and non-spatial auditory processing in the lateral intraparietal area. *Exp Brain Res* 162: 509-512, 2005.

Gifford III, G. W., Hauser, M. D. and Cohen, Y. E. Discrimination of functionally referential calls by laboratory-housed rhesus macaques: Implications for neuroethological studies. *Brain Behav Evol* 61: 213-224, 2003.

Gil-da-Costa, R., Braun, A., Lopes, M., Hauser, M. D., Carson, R. E., Herscovitch, P. and Martin, A. Toward an evolutionary perspective on conceptual representation: species-specific calls activate visual and affective processing systems in the macaque. *Proc Natl Acad Sci U S A* 101: 17516-21, 2004.

Graziano, M. S., Hu, X. T. and Gross, C. G. Coding the locations of objects in the dark. *Science* 277: 239-41, 1997.

Griffiths, T. D., Buchel, C., Frackowiak, R. S. and Patterson, R. D. Analysis of temporal structure in sound by the human brain. *Nat Neurosci* 1: 422-7, 1998.

Griffiths, T. D., Rees, G., Rees, A., Green, G. G. R., Witton, C., Rowe, D., Buchel, C., Turner, R. and Frackwiak, R. S. J. Right parietal cortex is involved in the perception of sound movement in humans. *Nat Neurosci* 1: 74-79, 1998.

Griffiths, T. D., Warren, J. D., Scott, S. K., Nelken, I. and King, A. J. Cortical processing of complex sound: a way forward? *Trends Neurosci* 27: 181-185, 2004.

Hackett, T. A., Preuss, T. M. and Kaas, J. H. Architectonic identification of the core region in auditory cortex of macaques, chimpanzees, and humans. *J Comp Neurol* 441: 197-222, 2001.

Hackett, T. A., Stepniewska, I. and Kaas, J. H. Subdivisions of auditory cortex and ipsilateral cortical connections of the parabelt auditory cortex in macaque monkeys. *J Comp Neurol* 394: 475-95, 1998.

Hackett, T. A., Stepniewska, I. and Kaas, J. H. Thalamocortical connections of the parabelt auditory cortex in macaque monkeys. *J Comp Neurol* 400: 271-86, 1998.

Hackett, T. A., Stepniewska, I. and Kaas, J. H. Prefrontal connections of the parabelt auditory cortex in macaque monkeys. *Brain Res* 817: 45-58, 1999.

Hart, H. C., Palmer, A. R. and Hall, D. A. Different areas of human non-primary auditory cortex are activated by sounds with spatial and nonspatial properties. *Hum Brain Mapp* 21: 178-204, 2004.

Hauser, M. D. Rhesus monkey copulation calls: honest signals for female choice? *Proc R Soc Lond B Biol Sci* 254: 93-6., 1993.

Hauser, M. D. The Evolution of Communication. MIT Press, Cambridge, MA, 1997.

Hauser, M. D. Functional referents and acoustic similarity: field playback experiments with rhesus monkeys. *Anim Behav* 55: 1647-1658, 1998.

Hauser, M. D., Evans, C. S. and Marler, P. The role of articulation in the production of rhesus monkey, Macaca mulatta, vocalizations. *Anim Behav* 4: 423-433, 1993.

Hauser, M. D. and Marler, P. Food-associated calls in rhesus macaques (*Macaca mulatta*) 1. Socioecological factors influencing call production. *Behav Ecol* 4: 194-205, 1993.

Hauser, M. D. and Marler, P. Food-associated calls in rhesus macaques (*Macaca mulatta*) II. Costs and benefits of call production and suppression. *Behav Ecol* 4, 1993.

Hinde, R. A. and Rowell, T. E. Communication by postures and facial expressions in the rhesus monkey (macaca mulatta). *Proc Zool Soc Lond* 138: 1-21, 1962.

Hyvärinen, J. Posterior parietal lobule of the primate brain. *Physiol Rev* 62: 1060-1129, 982.

Jurgens, U. Neural pathways underlying vocal control. *Neurosci Biobehav Rev.* 26: 235-58, 2002.

Jürgens, U. Neural pathways underlying vocal control. *Neurosci Biobehav Rev* 26: 235-258, 2002.

Kaas, J. H. and Hackett, T. A. Subdivisions of auditory cortex and levels of processing in primates. *Audiol Neurootol* 3: 73-85., 1998.

Kaas, J. H. and Hackett, T. A. 'What' and 'where' processing in auditory cortex. *nature neuroscience* 2: 1045-1047, 1999.

Kaas, J. H. and Hackett, T. A. Subdivisions of auditory cortex and processing streams in primates. *Proc Natl Acad Sci U S A* 97: 11793-9., 2000.

Kadia, S. C. and Wang, X. Spectral integration in A1 of awake primates: neurons with single- and multipeaked tuning characteristics. *J Neurophysiol* 89: 1603-22, 2003.

Kusunoki, M., Gottlieb, J. and Goldberg, M. E. The lateral intraparietal area as a salience map: the representation of abrupt onset, stimulus motion, and task relevance. *Vision Res* 40: 1459-68, 2000.

Logothetis, N. K. and Pauls, J. Psychophysical and physiological evidence for viewer-centered object representations in the primate. *Cerebral Cortex* 5: 270-88, 1995.

Lu, T., Liang, L. and Wang, X. Temporal and rate representations of time-varying signals in the auditory cortex of awake primates. *Nat Neurosci* 4: 1131-8, 2001.

Lu, T. and Wang, X. Information content of auditory cortical responses to time-varying acoustic stimuli. *J Neurophysiol* 91: 301-13, 2004.

Maeder, P. P., Meuli, R. A., Adriani, M., Bellmann, A., Fornari, E., Thiran, J. P., Pittet, A. and Clarke, S. Distinct pathways involved in sound recognition and localization: a human fMRI study. *Neuroimage* 14: 802-16, 2001.

Martin, A. and Chao, L. L. Semantic memory and the brain: structure and processes. *Curr Opin Neurobiol* 11: 194-201, 2001.

Middlebrooks, J. C. Auditory space processing: here, there or everywhere? *Nat Neurosci* 5: 824-826, 2002.

Miller, E. K. The prefrontal cortex and cognitive control. *Nat Rev Neurosci* 1: 59-65., 2000.

Miller, E. K., Freedman, D. J. and Wallis, J. D. The prefrontal cortex: categories, concepts, and cognition. *Philos Trans R Soc Lond B Biol Sci* 29: 1123-1136, 2002.

Milner, A. D. and Goodale, M. A. The Visual Brain in Action. Oxford Univ. Pres, Oxford, 1995.

Näätänen, R. Attention and Brain Function. Lawrence Erlbaum Associates, Hillsdale, NJ, 1992.

Owren, M. J. and Rendall, D. Salience of caller identity in rhesus monkey (Macaca mulatta) coos and screams: perceptual experiments with human (Homo sapiens) listeners. *J Comp Psychol* 117: 380-90, 2003.

Pandya, D. N. and Kuypers, H. G. Cortico-cortical connections in the rhesus monkey. *Brain Res* 13: 13-36, 1969.

Pandya, D. N. and Yeterian, E. H. in *Cerebral Cortex, Volume IV: Association and auditory cortices* (eds. A. Peters and E. G. Jones) 3-61 (Plenum Press, New York, 1985).

Partan, S. and Marler, P. Communication goes multimodal. *Science* 283: 1272-3, 1999.

Patterson, R. D., Johnsrude, I. S., Uppenkamp, S. and Griffiths, T. D. The processing of temporal pitch and melody information in auditory cortex. *Neuron* 36: 767-776, 2002.

Poremba, A., Saunders, R. C., Crane, A. M., Cook, M., Sokoloff, L. and Mishkin, M. Functional mapping of the primate auditory system. *Science* 299: 568-72, 2003.

Rämä, P., Poremba, A., Sala, J. B., Yee, L., Malloy, M., Mishkin, M. and Courtney, S. M. Dissociable functional topographics for working memory maintenance of voice identity and location. *Cereb Cortex* 14: 768-780, 2004.

Rao, S. C., Rainer, G. and Miller, E. K. Integration of what and where in the primate prefrontal cortex. *Science* 276: 821-4., 1997.

Rauschecker, J. P. and Tian, B. Mechanisms and streams for processing of "what" and "where" in auditory cortex. *PNAS* 97: 11800-11806, 2000.

Recanzone, G. H. Where was that? - human auditory spatial processing. *Trends Cogn Sci* 6: 319-320, 2002.

Rendall, D., Owren, M. J. and Rodman, P. S. The role of vocal tract filtering in identity cueing in rhesus monkey (Macaca mulatta) vocalizations. *J Acoust Soc Am* 103: 602-14, 1998.

Rendall, D., Owren, M. J., Weerts, E. and Hienz, R. D. Sex differences in the acoustic structure of vowel-like grunt vocalizations in baboons and their perceptual discrimination by baboon listeners. *J Acoust Soc Am* 115: 411-21, 2004.

Rendall, D., Rodman, P. S. and Emond, R. E. Vocal recognition of individuals and kin in free-ranging rhesus monkeys. *Animal Behavior* 51: 1007-1015, 1996.

Rivier, F. and Clarke, S. Cytochrome oxidase, acetylcholinesterase and NADPH-diaphorase staining in human supratemporal and insular cortex: evidence for multiple auditory areas. *Neuroimage* 6: 288-304, 1997.

Rizzuto, D. S., Mamelak, A. N., Sutherling, W. W., Fineman, I. and Andersen, R. A. Spatial selectivity in human ventrolateral prefrontal cortex. *Nat Neurosci* 8: 415-7, 2005.

Romanski, L. M., Averbeck, B. B. and Diltz, M. Neural representation of vocalizations in the primate ventrolateral prefrontal cortex. *J Neurophysiol* 93: 734-47, 2005.

Romanski, L. M., Bates, J. F. and Goldman-Rakic, P. S. Auditory belt and parabelt projections to the prefrontal cortex in the rhesus monkey. *J Comp Neurol* 403: 141-57., 1999.

Romanski, L. M. and Goldman-Rakic, P. S. An auditory domain in primate prefrontal cortex. *Nat Neurosci* 5: 15-6., 2002.

Romanski, L. M., Ojima, H., Fritz, J., Tian, B., Mishkin, M., Goldman-Rakic, P. and Rauschecker, J. Physiologically defined regions of the auditory belt cortex of the superior temporal gyrus target specific prefrontal regions in the rhesus monkey. *Society for Neuroscience Abstracts* 23: 2073, 1997.

Romanski, L. M., Tian, B., Fritz, J., Mishkin, M., Goldman-Rakic, P. S. and Rauschecker, J. P. Dual streams of auditory afferents target multiple domains in the primate prefrontal cortex. *Nat Neurosci* 2: 1131-6., 1999.

Romanski, L. M., Tian, B., Fritz, J. B., Mishkin, M., Goldman-Rakic, P. S. and Rauschecker, J. P. Reply to "What', 'where' and 'how' in auditory cortex'. *Nat Neurosci* 3: 966, 2000.

Schall, J. D., Morel, A., King, D. J. and Bullier, J. Topography of visual cortex connections with frontal eye field in macaque: convergence and segregation of processing streams. *J Neurosci* 15: 4464-87, 1995.

Scott, S. K., Blank, C. C., Rosen, S. and Wise, R. J. S. Identification of a pathway for intelligible speech in the left temporal lobe. *Brain* 123: 2400-2406, 2000.

Seltzer, B. and Pandya, D. N. Post-rolandic cortical projections of the superior temporal sulcus in the rhesus monkey. *J Comp Neurol* 312: 625-40., 1991.

Sereno, A. B. and Maunsell, J. H. Shape selectivity in primate lateral intraparietal cortex. *Nature* 395: 500-3., 1998.

Seyfarth, R. M., Cheney, D. L. and Marler, P. Monkey responses to three different alarm calls: evidence of predator classification and semantic communication. *Science* 210: 801-3, 1980.

Specht, K., Rimol, L. M., Reul, J. and Hugdahl, K. "Soundmorphing": a new approach to studying speech perception in humans. *Neurosci Lett* 384: 60-5, 2005.

Tardif, E. and Clarke, S. Intrinsic connectivity of human auditory areas: a tracing study with Dil. *Eur J Neurosci* 13: 1045-1050, 2001.

Toth, L. J. and Assad, J. A. Dynamic coding of behaviourally relevant stimuli in parietal cortex. *Nature* 415: 165-8., 2002.

Vouloumanos, A., Kiehl, K. A., Werker, J. F. and Liddle, P. F. Detection of sounds in the auditory stream: event-related fMRI evidence for differential activation to speech and nonspeech. *J Cogn Neurosci* 13: 994-1005, 2001.

Wang, X. On cortical coding of vocal communication sounds in primates. *PNAS* 97: 11843-11849, 2000.

Wang, X. and Kadia, S. C. Differential representation of species-specific primate vocalizations in the auditory cortices of marmoset and cat. *J Neurophysiol* 86: 2616-20., 2001.

Wang, X., Lu, T. and Liang, L. Cortical processing of temporal modulations. *Speech Communication* 41: 107-121, 2003.

Warren, J. D. and Griffiths, T. D. Distinct mechanisms for processing spatial sequences and pitch sequences in the human auditory brain. *J Neurosci* 23: 5799-5804, 2003.

Warren, J. D., Zielinski, B. A., Green, G. G., Rauschecker, J. P. and Griffiths, T. D. Perception of sound-source motion by the human brain. *Neuron* 34: 139-48, 2002.

Warren, J. E., Wise, R. J. and Warren, J. D. Sounds do-able: auditory-motor transformations and the posterior temporal plane. *Trends Neurosci* 28: 636-43, 2005.

Warrington, E. K. and Shallice, T. Category specific semantic impairments. *Brain* 107 (Pt 3): 829-54, 1984.

Webster, M. J., Bachevalier, J. and Ungerleider, L. G. Connections of inferior temporal areas TEO and TE with parietal and frontal cortex in macaque monkeys. *Cereb Cortex* 4: 470-83., 1994.

Zatorre, R. J., Bouffard, M., Ahad, P. and Belin, P. Where is 'where' in the human auditory cortex? *Nat Neurosci* 5: 905-9, 2002.

Zatorre, R. J., Evans, A. C., Meyer, E. and Gjedde, A. Lateralization of phonetic and pitch discrimination in speech processing. *Science* 256: 846-9, 1992.

Zuberbuhler, K. Causal cognition in a non-human primate: field playback experiments with Diana monkeys. *Cognition* 76: 195-207., 2000.

Zuberbuhler, K. Interspecies semantic communication in two forest primates. *Proc R Soc Lond B Biol Sci* 267: 713-8., 2000.

Zuberbuhler, K. Interspecies semantic communication in two forest primates. *Proc Biol Sci* 267: 713-8, 2000.

Zuberbuhler, K. and Seyfarth, R. M. Diana monkey long-distance calls: messages for conspecifics and predators. *Anim Behav* 53: 589-604, 1997.

In: Cognitive Sciences at the Leading Edge
Editor: Miao-Kun Sun, pp. 67-86

ISBN: 978-1-60456-051-0
© 2008 Nova Science Publishers, Inc.

Chapter 6

ROLE OF ENDOPLASMIC RETICULUM-MEDIATED APOPTOTIC PATHWAY IN Aβ TOXICITY

Elisabete Ferreiro, Rui Costa, Sueli Marques,
*Catarina R. Oliveira and Cláudia M. F. Pereira**

Center for Neurosciences and Cell Biology,
Institute of Biochemistry, Faculty of Medicine,
University of Coimbra, 3004-504 Coimbra, Portugal

ABSTRACT

The endoplasmic reticulum (ER) plays an essential role in normal cell functioning and also in the pathogenesis of neuronal death. Irreparable perturbations in the homeostasis of the ER and alterations that lead to the accumulation of unfolded or misfolded protein in the ER lumen are thought to trigger several signalling pathways to restore the homeostasis of this organelle. These processes have been described to be involved in different important human diseases, including Alzheimer's disease (AD). Increasing evidences points to apoptosis as the major mechanism responsible for the neuronal death that occurs in this neurodegenerative disorder. In this context, mitochondrial dysfunction has been widely studied as a pathway integrated in the apoptosis that occurs in AD. It is an increasing assumption that the ER and the mitochondria cooperate in the mechanisms responsible for neuronal death and evidences suggest that mitochondria/ER crosstalk is also involved in AD. The recent and the novel research on ER stress and mitochondrial dysfunction and the cooperation between these two pathways can enhance the understanding of the molecular mechanisms that occur in AD and provide potential therapeutical targets.

---

* Correspondence and requests for reprints: Cláudia M.F. Pereira, Institute of Biochemistry, Faculty of Medicine, University of Coimbra, 3004-504 Coimbra, Portugal. Telephone: +351-239820190; Fax: +351-239822776. E-mail: cpereira@cnc.cj.uc.pt

Keywords: *Alzheimer's disease, amyloid-β peptide, apoptosis, endoplasmic reticulum stress.*

ABBREVIATIONS

Aβ	amyloid-beta peptide;
ABAD	Abeta-binding alcohol dehydrogenase;
AD	Alzheimer's disease;
AIF	apoptosis-inducing factor;
APP	amyloid precursor protein;
Ask1	apoptosis-signal-regulating-kinase-1;
ATF4	activating transcription factor 4;
ATF6	activating transcription factor 6;
CICR	Ca^{2+}-induced Ca^{2+} release;
eIF2α	eukaryotic initiation factor-2 alpha;
ER	endoplasmic reticulum;
ERAD	ER-associated protein degradation;
GRP78	glucose-regulated protein 78;
InsP3R	inositol 1,4,5-triphosphate receptor;
IRE1	inositol requiring transmembrane kinase/endonuclease;
JNK	c-Jun N-terminal kinase;
PERK	RNA-dependent protein kinase (PKR)-like ER membrane-localized kinase;
PS1	presenilin-1;
PS2	presenilin-2;
ROS	reactive oxygen species;
RyR	ryanodine receptor;
SERCA	sarco-endoplasmic reticulum ATPase;
TRAF2	TNF-associated factor 2;
UPR	Unfolded Protein Response.

1. ENDOPLASMIC RETICULUM AS AN ESSENTIAL ORGANELLE IN THE CELL

1.1. ER Function and Localization

The endoplasmic reticulum (ER) is an organelle found in all eukaryotic cells, and is an interconnected network of tubules, vesicles and cisternae, responsible for several specialized functions: protein translation, folding, and transport of proteins to be used in the cell membrane, or to be secreted from the cell; sequestration of calcium; and production and storage of glycogen, steroids, and other macromolecules (Baumann and Walz, 2001). The general structure of the ER is an extensive membrane network of cisternae held together by the cytoskeleton. The functions of the ER vary greatly depending on the exact type of ER and the type of cell in which it resides. Three types of ER can be found in cells: rough ER, smooth ER, and sarcoplasmic reticulum. The last one is a subtype of smooth ER and can be found in striated muscle, the main function being the pump and store of Ca^{2+} ions. Both rough and smooth ER are continuous with the outer layer of the nuclear envelope. The rough ER owns is name to its association to ribossomes, giving a "rough" appearance and is responsible for protein synthesis. The rough ER works in concert with the Golgi complex to target new proteins to their proper destinations. The smooth ER has functions in several metabolic processes, including synthesis of lipids, metabolism of carbohydrates and Ca^{2+} concentration. The network of smooth ER allows increased surface area for the action or storage of several proteins (Baumann and Walz, 2001).

In neurons, ER is widely distributed, being present in dendrites and dendric spines, axons and presynaptic nerve terminals and in growth cones (Cheng and Reese, 1985; Deitch and banker, 1993; Kanaseki et al., 1998; Levesque et al., 1999; Dailey and Bridgman, 1989). Although smooth and rough ER coexist in neuronal cell bodies and proximal regions of axons and dendrites, the specialized endings of neuritis contain mainly smooth ER (Mattson et al., 2000).

1.2. When the ER Becomes Stressed

1.2.1. ER and the Unfolded Protein Response

As referred above, one of the main functions of ER is the synthesis, modification and delivery of proteins to their proper target sites within the secretory pathway and extracellular space. In the ER, proteins fold into their native conformation and undergo several post-translational modifications (Schröder and Kaufman, 2005). Only correctly folded proteins are exported to the Golgi complex. When unfolded proteins accumulate in the ER, the adaptive ER stress response is triggered and several signalling pathways are activated. This adaptive response is known as the Unfolded Protein Response (UPR) (Kaufman, 1999; Mori, 2000; Patil et al., 2001; Kaufman 2002). The UPR comprises a chain of reactions that attenuates protein translation, elevates expression of ER chaperones and upregulates proteins needed for ER-associated degradation (ERAD) (Rutkowski and Kaufman, 2004). Three distinct signalling pathways are activated in the UPR, mediated by the sensors: IRE1 (inositol requiring transmembrane kinase/endonuclease), composed of two identified homologues IRE1α (Tirasophon et al., 1998) and IRE1β (Wang et al., 1998), PERK (RNA-dependent protein Kinase (PKR)-like ER membrane-localized kinase) and ATF6 (activating transcription factor 6) (Harding et al., 1999; Liu et al., 2000; Nadanaka et al., 2007) (Fig.1). In normal conditions, the luminal domains of these sensors are occupied by BiP/GRP78, an ER HSP70 family protein, that as high affinity for protein substrates, and represses the three signalling pathways. When the unfolded proteins accumulate in the lumen of the ER, they competitively disrupt the interaction of BiP/GRP78 with IRE1, PERK and ATF6, activating the three signalling pathways (Shröder and Kaufman, 2005). IRE1 pathway regulates chaperone induction, expansion of the ER and ERAD in response to ER stress. After the dissociation of BiP/GRP78, IRE1 oligomerizes (Shamu and Walter, 1996; Liu et al., 2002) and initiates unconventional splicing of an mRNA encoding the basic leucine zipper (bZIP)-type transcription factor XBP1 that controls the up-regulation of a subset of ER-resident molecular chaperones (Iwakoshi et al., 2003; Mori 2000; Schröder and Kaufman, 2005; Lee et al., 2003). After being released by BiP/GRP78, PERK oligomerizes and phosphorylates the eIF2α (eukaryotic initiation factor-2 alpha) (Harding et al. 1999; Shi et al., 1998; Shi et al., 1999). Phosphorylartion of eIF2α results in the attenuation of global mRNA translation (Harding et al. 1999) and activates translation of ATF4 (activating transcription factor 4), a transcription factor that induces expression of genes, depending on the environmental stress, that function in amino acid metabolism, in antioxidant response and apoptosis (Harding et al., 2000; 2003; Lu et al., 2004; Vattem and Wek 2004). ATF6 is a Type 2 transmembrane protein, composed of a cytosolic NH2-terminal domain (a transcription factor of the basic-leucine zipper, bZip, family), followed by a transmembrane domain and an extracytoplasmic domain that projects into the ER lumen (Haze et al., 1999). Upon ER stress, cleaved ATF6 is transported from the ER to the Golgi complex to be processed by the sequential action of Site-1 protease (S1P) and Site-2 protease (S2P) (Ye et al., 2000; Okada et al., 2003). Cleaved ATF6 (p50 ATF6) translocates to the nucleus where it activates the transcription of genes encoding ER-localized molecular chaperones, like BiP/GRP78, GRP94, and calnexin and several folding enzymes (Yoshida et al. 2001; Yoshida et al. 2002; Nadanaka et al., 2007). If these signalling pathways fail to relieve the ER stress, the IRE1-mediated upregulation of ubiquitination enzymes belonging to the ERAD machinery will take place to target misfolded proteins for degradation (Yoshida et al., 2003; Hampton, 2003). Upregulation of ERAD components may be the last resort to deal with ER stress-induced accumulation of misfolded proteins in the ER (Shen et al., 2007). Finally, when cells are not able to adapt to the extensive ER stress, several mechanisms of cell death are activated.

1.2.2. ER and Calcium Homeostasis

ER is the major storage place of intracellular Ca^{2+} of the cell, which can be activated by both electrical and chemical cell stimulation (Bootman et al., 2002; Berridge, 2002; Verkhratsky and Petersen, 2002). The total concentration of Ca^{2+} in the ER lumen is estimated to be 1–3mM, similar to that in the extracellular space, and most of this is bound to chaperones, such as calreticulin, calnexin, BiP, GRP94 and calumin (Meldolesi and Pozzan, 1998; Michalak et al., 2002; Zhang et al., 2007). Nevertheless, a significant portion of Ca^{2+} in the lumen is free. The free concentration of Ca^{2+} in the ER ranges from 60 to 400 μM when stores are full, and from 1 to 50 μM when they are empty (Meldolesi and Pozzan, 1998; Corbett and Michalak, 2000). The release of Ca^{2+} from ER store regulates a variety of cellular events and processes, for example excitation-concentration coupling in muscle, regulation of genes expression, neuronal plasticity, neurotransmitter release and exocytosis (Niggli, 1999; Hardingham et al., 2001, Freguenlli et al., 1996; Rose and Konnerth, 2001). Release of Ca^{2+} from the ER is controlled by channels like the inositol-1,4,5-trisphosphate receptor (InsP$_3$R) and the ryanodine receptor (RyR) families (Berridge, 1993; Clapham, 1995) (Figure 1).

Ca^{2+} is the principal activator of these channels, in a process called Ca^{2+}-induced Ca^{2+} release (CICR) (Iino, 1990). Ca^{2+} is released from the InsP$_3$R in response to agonists that activate receptors coupled, via a GTP-binding protein, to phospholipase C (PLC). Activation of PLC results in cleavage of PtdIns(4,5)P2, which in turn results in the liberation of diacylglycerol and Ins(1,4,5)P$_3$ that binds to InsP$_3$R. Opening of the InsP$_3$ receptor depends simultaneously of the presence of both InsP$_3$ and Ca^{2+} (Finch et al., 1991).

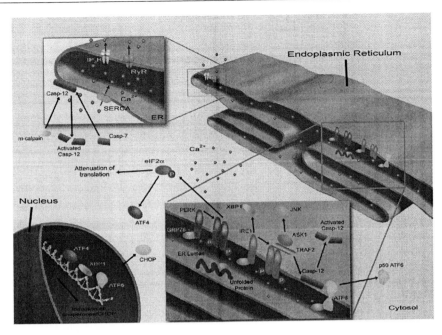

Figure 1. Mechanism of cell survival and cell death in response to ER stress. Accumulation of unfolded proteins in the ER activates the ER stress sensors, such as IRE1, ATF6 and PERK, which mediates ER stress response. Dissociation of BiP/GRP78 from stress transducers leads to oligomerization and autophosphorylation of IRE1 and PERK. Oligomerized IRE1 initiates unconventional splicing of an mRNA encoding the basic leucine zipper (bZIP)-type transcription factor XBP1. Phosphorylated PERK phosphorylates eIF2α, which attenuates global mRNA translation and activates translation of ATF4. Dissociation of BiP/GRP78 from ATF6 allows this protein to be cleaved by S1P and S2P. Cleaved ATF6 (p50 ATF6) translocates to the nucleus where, together with ATF4, XBP1 activate the transcription of genes encoding ER-localized molecular chaperones. Release of Ca^{2+} from the ER is controlled by channels like the RyR and InsP3R. SERCA is responsible for the return of Ca^{2+} to the internal stores. If ER Ca^{2+} homeostasis is altered, accumulation of unfolded proteins can lead to UPR. Prolonged ER stress triggers ER-mediated apoptotic pathway, leading to cell death. Activated IRE1α binds TRAF2, which in turn activates the Ask1 and subsequently JNK. ATF6 translocates to the nucleus and activates several genes, namely CHOP/GADD153, decreasing the expression of Bcl-2. On the other hand, PERK/eIF2α and IRE1/TRAF2/Ask1 pathways increase CHOP/GADD153 activity at a posttranscriptional level. TRAF-2 interacts with procaspase-12 and promotes its activation. Procaspase-12 can also be cleaved by Ca^{2+}-activated m-calpains and by caspase-7.

In the presence of low concentrations of Ca^{2+} (100–300 nM) the channel is more sensitive to InsP3, whereas at concentrations above 300 nM, Ca^{2+} becomes inhibitory (Bootman and Lipp, 1999). RyR reside in close proximity to the cell membrane and respond to Ca^{2+} influx through voltage-gated Ca^{2+} channels and also to Ca^{2+} released from the InsP3R. RyR channels contain two different Ca^{2+} binding sites, with high and low affinity for the cation. As for InsP3R, at low Ca^{2+} concentrations RyR are activated and at high Ca^{2+} concentrations the activity is inhibited (Wrzosek, 2000).

The autocatalytic process of CICR enables the InsP3Rs and RyRs to communicate with each other to establish coordinated Ca^{2+} signals (Berridge et al., 2002). In neurons, RyR-mediated signals are more pronounced in dendritic spines and presynaptic terminals (Padua et al., 1996; Rose and Konnerth 2001), and InsP3R and InsP3-evoked signals are predominantly localized in the soma and proximal dendrites of cortical and hippocampal neurons (Sharp et al., 1993; Nakamura et al., 1999; Stutzmann et al., 2003).

When the Ca^{2+} signalling has reached the purpose by which it was triggered, it is rapidly removed from the cytoplasm by various pumps (Pozzan et al., 1994) and exchangers (Blaustein and Lederer, 1999). The plasma membrane Ca^{2+}-ATPase (PMCA) pumps and Na^+/Ca^{2+} exchangers extrude Ca^{2+} to the outside. The sarco-endoplasmic reticulum ATPase (SERCA) pumps return Ca^{2+} to the internal stores (Fig. 1). The mitochondrion is another important component by sequestering Ca^{2+} rapidly during the development of the Ca^{2+} signal and releasing it back slowly during the recovery phase (Budd and Nicholls, 1996).

In the same way that ER Ca^{2+} is involved in Ca^{2+} signalling, the high Ca^{2+} concentration found in the ER is also important for the folding and processing of newly synthesized proteins, since these are strictly Ca^{2+}-dependent reactions requiring high Ca^{2+} activity for correct functioning (Kuznetsov et al., 1992; Lodish et al., 1992). If ER Ca^{2+} homeostasis is altered, accumulation of unfolded proteins can lead to UPR and consequently activate the ER-stress-induced apoptosis pathway (Kaufman, 1999; Pashen, 2001).

1.2.3. ER-Stress-Induced Apoptotic Pathway

Prolonged ER stress triggers ER-mediated apoptotic pathway, leading to cell death (Fig. 1). In the numerous studies performed to elucidate the ER-mediated cell death, pharmalogical agents have been used to induce ER stress, either by inducing UPR (like brefeldin A, an ER-Golgi transport inhibitor or tunicamycin, a N-linked glycosylation inhibitor) or by perturbating ER Ca^{2+} homeostasis (like thapsigargin, an inhibitor of SERCA/Ca^{2+}ATPase).

As a response of UPR, activated IRE1α can bind to the protein TRAF2 (TNF-associated factor 2), activating protein kinases, like Ask1 (apoptosis-signal-regulating-kinase-1), which can trigger the c-Jun N-terminal kinase (JNK) pathway (Urano et al., 2000; Nishitoh et al., 2002). Furthermore, ATF6 translocates to the nucleus and activates several genes, namely CHOP/GADD153, a transcription factor that decreases the expression of the anti-apoptotic protein Bcl-2 (McCullough et al, 2001). In addition, PERK/eIF2α pathway and IRE1/TRAF2/Ask1 pathway can increase CHOP/GADD153 activity at a posttranscriptional level (Wang and Ron, 1996). Activation of the JNK, triggered by IRE1, can also increase the levels of the proapoptotic protein Bim (Lei and Davis, 2003; Putcha et al., 2003) and decrease the Bcl-2 protein levels (Yamamoto, 1999). In rodents, Ire1-α, through the recruitment of TRAF-2, can lead to the activation of caspase-12. TRAF-2 interacts with procaspase-12 and promotes its clustering and its activation (Yoneda et al., 2001). Pro-caspase-12 is specifically localized on the cytoplasmic side of the ER and can also be proteolytically activated by m-calpain, a Ca^{2+}-responsive cytosolic cysteine protease (Nakagawa and Yuan, 2000). Caspase-12 may also by activated by caspase-7, which translocates this caspase from the ER to the cytosol (Rao et al., 2001). The involvement of caspase-12 in the apoptosis induced by ER stress has been widely contested, due to its absence in most humans (Fischer et al., 2002). The closest homolog of pro-caspase-12 in humans is pro-caspase-4 that has been suggested to be involved in ER stress-induced apoptosis (Hitomi et al., 2004). However, Obeng and Boise, in 2005, have shown that caspase-12 and caspase-4 are not required for the induction of ER stress-induced apoptosis and that caspase-4-like activity is not always associated with an initiating event. Recently, caspase-2 has been proposed to have an important role in the initiation of ER-induced apoptosis (Cheung et al., 2006). The authors propose that activation of caspase-2, which seems to be located partially in the ER, may integrate the apoptotic signalling between the ER and the Golgi complex and also acts as an upstream signalling to permeabilize the outer mitochondrial membrane. Furthermore, caspase-8, an initiator caspase that has been linked to the Death Receptors (TNF receptor and the Fas receptor) (Ashkenazi, 2002), was shown to be activated by thapsigargin, leading to cleavage of the pro-apoptotic BH3-only protein Bid, and thus to be involved in ER-stress-mediated cell death (He et al., 2002).

Several evidences suggest that mitochondria have an important role in the ER-mediated cell death and that these two organelles have a close cooperation in the process. First, apoptotic stimuli known to act through Ca^{2+} release from the ER induce a prolonged increase in the mitochondrial Ca^{2+} concentration, which can activate the permeability transition pore (PTP) (Szalai et al., 1999). This membrane channel can facilitate mitochondrial swelling and disruption of mitochondrial permeability transition (MPT) leading to the release of cytochrome c, AIF (apoptosis-inducing factor), several procaspases and Smac-α/DIABLO (Pinton et al., 2000; Bernardi et al., 2001), thereby facilitating the formation of the apoptosome that activates caspase-9, which ultimately activates caspase-3 and caspase-7 (Ferri and Kroemer, 2001). Beside having a role in the mitochondrial-mediated apoptosis, various proteins of the BCL-2 family modulate Ca^{2+} content regulation by both mitochondria and ER. Overexpression of the antiapoptotic protein Bcl-2 modulates Ca^{2+} signalling, by decreasing the ER Ca^{2+} load and consequently protecting the cells from death (Foyouzi-Youssefi et al., 2000; Pinton et al., 2000). Conversely, the pro-apoptotic Bax/Bak proteins overexpression favors the transfer of Ca^{2+} from ER to mitochondria and induces cell death (Nutt et al., 2002a,b; Scorrano et al., 2003). Cytochrome c, released from mitochondria, can also bind to and promote Ca^{2+} release through the InsP3R in the ER membrane. The released Ca^{2+} triggers the extrusion of a large amount of cytochrome c from all the mitochondria in the cell, amplifying the death signal (Boehning et al., 2003; 2004; Wang and El-Deiry, 2004).

In the cooperation between ER and mitochondria in inducing apoptosis, the role of reactive oxygen species (ROS) cannot be forgotten. ROS can be produced in mitochondria, which are thought to be the major source of ROS in vivo (Boveris and Chance, 1973) and by the ER (Chan, 1996). Several studies have demonstrated that the ER is sensitive to oxidative stress (Dreher et al., 1995; Racay et al., 1995) and oxidative stress may lead to perturbations of the ER Ca^{2+} homeostasis because many of the proteins involved in the regulation of Ca^{2+} in the ER, such as InsP3R and RyR, Ca^{2+} ATPases and ER-resident proteins, are sensitive to oxidants (Huang et al., 2004). Furthermore, CHOP/GADD153 can lead to the transcription of the ER oxiredutase ERO1α, which participates in protein disulfide bond during protein folding formation and protein refolding in the ER (to help relieve ER stress), and consequently lead to the transfer of electrons to molecular oxygen, forming ROS (Marciniak et al., 2004). In addition, Ca^{2+} that results from the depletion of ER Ca^{2+} stores can be taken up by juxtaposed mitochondria, inducing ROS formation (Tardif et al., 2005).

2. ER STRESS IN ALZHEIMER'S DISEASE

ER stress as been associated to several diseases, including ischemia/reperfusion, inflammation, diabetes and neurodegerative diseases like Parkinson's, Prion's and Alzheimer's diseases (Hetz et al., 2003; Xu et al., 2005; Zhao and Ackerman, 2006).

Alzheimer's disease (AD), the most common form of senile dementia, is a progressive neurodegenerative disease of the central nervous system, characterized by insidious, chronic and progressive memory impairment. A defining feature of AD is the accumulation of amyloid-β (Aβ; Mattson, 1997), a 39–43-aminoacid peptide derived from the amyloid precursor protein (APP; Wisniewski et al., 1997). The importance of Aβ in the pathogenesis of AD is suggested by several findings. Notably, mutations in APP or presenilin-1 and -2 (PS1 and PS2, respectively), two proteins that are implicated in familiar forms of AD, lead to an increase in the amyloidogenic forms of Aβ (Selkoe, 1999). APP is first cleaved by β-secretase at the N-terminus of Aβ, followed by an intramembranous cleavage at the C-terminus of Aβ by the γ-secretase, resulting two principal products, Aβ1–40 and Aβ1–42 that have been shown to be toxic to a wide variety of cells, including neurons (Yankner, 1996). Accumulating evidence suggest that PS1, a transmembrane domain aspartyl protease that is mainly located in the ER, together with three other membrane proteins (nicastrin, APH-1 and PEN-2) form the γ-secretase complex (reviewed in Steiner and Haass, 2000; Mattson, 2003). More recently, APP localization was reported to be altered under ER stress, being translocated from late compartments to early compartments of the secretory pathway, consequently leading to the decrease of the levels of Aβ1–40 and Aβ1–42 by β and γ-cutting, suggesting a possible early cellular defensive mechanism to reduce Aβ levels (Kudo et al., 2006). Furthermore, cells that express mutant mutant PS1 have been reported to be more sensitive to apoptotic stimuli, especially ER stress (Guo et al., 1997; 1999 a,b).

Several data have linked UPR to AD. In 2005, Hoozemans and co-workers have reported that the levels of Bip/GRP78 were increased in the temporal cortex and hippocampus of post-mortem brain tissues of AD patients. Furthemore, they found phosphorylated PERK (p-PERK, the active form of PERK) in AD brain tissues, suggesting UPR involvement in AD. Furthermore, Aβ1–42 was also shown to induce ER stress, by increasing the levels of the ER chaperones, Bip/GRP78 and GRP94 and also to increase the activity of the transcription factor CHOP/GADD153 (Ghribi et al., 2004). We have also recently showed that in primary cortical neurons the peptide Aβ1–40 was able to induce the increase the levels of Bip/GRP78, inducing in this manner ER stress (Ferreiro et al., 2006) (Figure 2). In addition, in cholinergic neurons, soluble oligomeric Aβ1–42 forms were shown to affect genes of proteins present in the ER and Golgi-complex involved in protein modification and degradation, like several chaperones and ATF6, being an additional proof for the involvement of the UPR and ER stress in Aβ toxicity (Heinitz et al., 2006).

In addition to the link of UPR to AD, several evidences show that perturbation of ER Ca^{2+} homeostasis is also an important step in the beginning or progress of the neuronal death that occurs in the disease. In 2000, Leissring find out that the presenilins, located in the ER membrane, not only function to process the APP but also modulate Ca^{2+} signalling. Mutations of presenilin result in overfilling of the ER leading to larger Ca^{2+} signals and a decrease in capacitative Ca^{2+} entry. Recently, overexpression of APP was shown to potently enhance cytosolic Ca^{2+} levels and cell death after ER Ca^{2+} store depletion and the transcription factor CHOP was significantly upregulated in these conditions (Copanaki et al., 2007). Furthermore, experiments in cortical neurons from mutant PS1 knock-in mice demonstrated the potentiation of ER Ca^{2+} liberation by photoreleased $InsP_3$ and altered membrane excitability (Stutzmann et al., 2003, 2004). More recently, Stutzmann and co-wokers have shown that neurons from young, adult, and aged AD mice have enhanced RyR recruitment, given by the higher levels of RyR expression, that contribute to the exaggerated Ca^{2+} signals (Stutzmann et al., 2006). In addition, in neurons from PS1 knock-in mice and 3xTg-AD mice that harbor mutant genes: presenilin-1 (PS1M146V), APP (bAPPswe) and tau P301L transgenes) enhanced Ca^{2+} response was associated with the increased levels of RyR (Smith et al., 2005). Several studies have shown that the Aβ peptide is also responsible for Ca^{2+} homeostasis perturbation (Figure 2). Aβ1-42 was observed to mediate changes in intracellular Ca^{2+} homeostasis, through a direct increase of the RyR3 isorfom expression and function (Supnet et al., 2006).

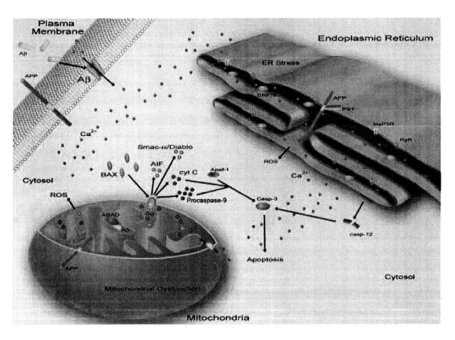

Figure 2. Endoplasmic reticulum-mediated apoptotic pathway in Aβ toxicity. Accumulation of excessive Aβ peptide, due to increase generation through the amyloidogenic processing of APP or decreased clearance, can increase cytosolic Ca^{2+} levels, possibly due to the formation of Aβ oligomers, which assemble into Ca^{2+} channels as they interact with the cell surface, and/or to the increase RyRs levels, increasing Ca^{2+} release from ER. Furthermore, mutated presenilins located at the ER membrane are responsible for the overfilling of the ER leading to larger Ca^{2+} signals. Overexpression of APP also strongly enhances cytosolic Ca^{2+} levels and the transcription factor CHOP. Therefore, Aβ leads to the perturbation of Ca^{2+} homeostasis, can induce UPR, ER stress and activation of caspase-12, which can trigger apoptotic cell death. The ER-mediated apoptotic pathway may then proceed through a mitochondrial process. Due to the close proximity of both organelles, Ca^{2+} released from the ER can perturb Ca^{2+} homeostasis in the mitochondria, initiating the mitochondrial cell death pathway, involving translocation of Bax, release of apoptotic factors (cytochrome-c, AIF) and activation of caspases cascade. Moreover, processed Aβ formed in the mitochondria or imported to this organelle can interact with ABAD protein potentiating mitochondrial dysfunction. Finally, Aβ peptide is also responsible for the formation of ROS, from the ER and/or from the mitochondria, increasing its toxic effects.

Several studies argue that the perturbation in Ca^{2+} homeostasis can be due to an early formation of membranar Aβ calcium channel, suggesting a possible initiating mechanism of Aβ toxicity as a death message that can be extended to the ER. In fact, morphological and intracellular Ca^{2+} changes in fibroblasts and endothelial cells are apparent 10-15 min after treatment with freshly prepared Aβ solutions. These early effects have been linked to the formation of nascent Aβ calcium channel (Bathia et al., 2000). In addition, Simakova and Arispe (2006) have shown that exposure of cells to Aβ results in the initial formation of oligomeric Aβ aggregates which assemble Ca^{2+} channels as they interact with the cell surface membrane (Figure 2). In cortical neurons treated with Aβ1-40, an increase in the intracellular Ca^{2+} concentration was observed, due to the early release of ER Ca^{2+} through RyR and InsP3R, activating ER stress (Ferreiro et al., 2004, 2006). As a response of Aβ-induced ER stress several mechanism are activated. Caspase-12 in rodents and human caspase-4 were shown to be activated by Aβ peptide (Nakagawa et al., 2000; Ferreiro et al., 2006; Hitomi et al., 2004). Furthermore, due to the Ca^{2+} release through RyR and $InsP_3R$ we have shown that Aβ1-40 induces the formation of ROS, cytochrome c release from mitochondria, caspase-3 activation and cell death (Ferreiro et al., 2006) (Figure 2).

Several studies have point to mitochondria dysfunction as fundamental phenomenon in AD (Cardoso et al., 2001; Cardoso et al., 2002; for review see Reddy and Beal, 2005 and Bubber et al., 2005) (Fig.2). In fact, accumulation of full-length APP in the mitochondria compartment can cause mitochondrial dysfunction and impaired energy metabolism (Anandatheerthavarada et al., 2003) In addition, Aβ was shown to accumulate within mitochondria and such accumulation to be associated to mitochondrial dysfunction (Caspersen et al., 2005). Furthermore, Aβ can enter mitochondria inducing free radicals generation and mitochondrial dysfunction (Reddy, 2006). Aβ can also interact with Aβ-binding alcohol dehydrogenase (ABAD) in the mitochondria and this interaction promotes leakage of ROS, mitochondrial dysfunction and cell death (Lustbader et al., 2004).

One possible site of initiation of apoptosis is the synapse. Perturbed synaptic ER Ca^{2+} homeostasis was shown to promote activation of apoptotic cascades (Mattson, 2000). Although $InsP_3Rs$ are mostly found in dendritic shafts and cell bodies, levels of RyRs are highest in axons and dendritic spines (Padua et al., 1992; Padua et al., 1996). Since RyRs are overexpressed and have increased activity in AD brain, these channels may have responsible for synaptic dysfunction and loss that characterize AD (Selkoe, 2002).

Many questions related to the initial mechanistic process that leads to cell death in AD remain to be answered. Nonetheless, there is increasing evidence that ER stress is involved in the process and that both ER and mitochondria (and possibly also other organelles) cooperate in the neuronal cell that occurs in this disease.

3. POTENTIAL THERAPEUTICS

Only two classes of medication are currently available for AD patients, confined to symptomatic palliative interventions, namely the acetylcholinesterase inhibitors and the N-methyl-D-aspartate receptor antagonist memantine. Both classes have modest clinical benefits and do not prevent disease progression. Therefore, it is imperative to develop effective therapies that halt or reverse the underlying disease process.

The recent evidences that demonstrate the role of ER dysfunction in AD, support that ER may be a target for therapeutic intervention. Neuroprotective strategies, designed to reduce specifically Ca^{2+} release through RyR with dantrolene (inhibitor of RyRs) or using lithium to slow IP3 turnover (Ferreiro et al., 2006; Devaki et al, 2006), are promising therapeutical targets. In addition, the use of Ca^{2+} chelators, like BAPTA-AM can provide an additional help to reduce intracellular Ca^{2+}. In fact, BAPTA has been shown to block Ca^{2+} levels increase and to inhibit procaspase-12 cleavage (Sokka et al., 2007). Furthermore, manipulation of expression and function of anti-apoptotic Bcl-2 family members, that have been shown to be present in the ER and to regulate ER Ca^{2+} homeostasis, may also bring some improvement to the protection of neurons. Indeed, treatment strategies that are currently being developed include the delivery of anti-apoptotic Bcl-2 family members, small molecule inhibitors that interact directly with Bcl-2 family members, including both endogenously synthetic agents, which increase indirectly the overall expression and/or function of anti-apoptotic Bcl-2 family members (reviewed in Shacka and Roth, 2005). In addition, targeted anti-apoptotic Bcl-2 and Bcl-xL to the ER may also represent a therapeutical tool to regulate ER Ca^{2+} homeostasis.

The accumulation of unfolded proteins has also been a target of the therapeutical strategies. In fact, to diminish the accumulation of unfolded proteins that normally occurs in the ER stress condition, several authors studied the potential use of chemical chaperones (Perlmutter, 2002; Cohen and Kelly, 2003; Romisch, 2004; Welch, 2004). These small organic compounds have chaperone-like activities and have the capacity to assist in the correct folding/assembly of unfolded proteins. The use of drugs that up-regulate the expression of ER stress proteins like GRP78, for example valproate (Wang and Young, 2004), or by stimulating ERAD, which could lead to an improvement in the folding capacity (Mori, 2000). Furthermore, selective chemical inhibitors of eIF2alpha dephosphorylation, like Salubrinal, may be useful to reduce ER stress (Boyce et al., 2005).

Another possibility to reduce the effects of ER stress has been the attempt to reduce oxidative stress that occurs upon this process. Application of exogenous antioxidants, like α-tocopherol (vitamin E) and polyphenols (Floyd, 1999), mobilization of endogenous antioxidant such as glutathione (Butterfield, 2002) or scavengers of oxygen-free radicals (Oyadomari and Mori, 2004) have been tested to reduce intracellular ROS levels. Besides, application of ER-targeted antioxidants may be useful to reduce ROS levels, which are formed in the ER.

The present knowledge of how AD begins and progresses must be enlarged in order to find new therapeutical strategies to delay or prevent the neuronal death that occurs during progression of this devastating disease.

ACKNOWLEDGEMENTS

This work was supported by FCT (Portuguese Research Council) project nº POCTI/36101/NSE/2000 and PhD fellowships nº SFRH/BD/14108/2003 and SFRH/BD/28403/2006. We thank João Cardoso (Department of Physics, Faculty of Science and Tecnology, University of Coimbra) for the contribution in the figure design.

REFERENCES

Anandatheerthavarada, H.K., Biswas, G., Robin, M.A., Avadhani, N.G. Mitochondrial targeting and a novel transmembrane arrest of Alzheimer's amyloid precursor protein impairs mitochondrial function in neuronal cells. *J. Cell Biol.* 161: 41-54, 2003.

Ashkenazi, A. Targeting death and decoy receptors of the tumour-necrosis factor superfamily. *Nat. Rev. Cancer.* 2: 420–430, 2002.

Bathia, R., Lin, H., Lal, R. Fresh and globular amyloid β protein induces rapid cellular degeneration. A possible implication for calcium-uptake via AβP-channel, *FASEB J.* 14: 1233-1243, 2000.

Baumann, O., Walz, B. Endoplasmic reticulum of animal cells and its organization into structural and functional domains. *Int. Rev. Cytol. 205:* 149-214, 2001.

Bernardi, P, Petronilli, V, Di Lisa, F, Forte, M. A mitochondrial perspective on cell death. *Trends Biochem. Sci.* 26: 112-117, 2001.

Berridge, M. J. Inositol trisphosphate and calcium signalling. *Nature* 361: 315-325, 1993.

Berridge, M.J. The endoplasmic reticulum: a multifunctional signalling organelle. *Cell Calcium* 32: 235-249, 2002.

Blaustein, M.P.   Lederer, W.J. Sodium/calcium exchange: Its physiological implications. *Physiol. Rev.* 79: 763–854, 1999.

Boehning, D., Patterson, R.L., Sedaghat, L., Glebova, N.O., Kurosaki, T., Snyder, S.H. Cytochrome c binds to inositol (1,4,5) trisphosphate receptors, amplifying calcium-dependent apoptosis. *Nat. Cell Biol.* 5: 1051-61, 2003.

Boehning, D, Patterson, RL, Snyder, SH. Apoptosis and calcium: new roles for cytochrome c and inositol 1,4,5-trisphosphate. *Cell Cycle* 3: 252-254(2004).

Bootman, M.D., Lipp, P. Calcium signalling: Ringing changes to the 'bell-shaped curve. *Curr. Biol.* 9: R876–R878, 1999.

Bootman, M.D., Petersen, O.H. , Verkhratsky, A. The endoplasmic reticulum is a focal point for co-ordination of cellular activity. *Cell Calcium* 32: 231-234, 2002.

Boveris, A., Chance, B. The mitochondrial generation of hydrogen peroxide. General properties and effect of hyperbaric oxygen. *Biochem. J.* 134: 707-716, 1973.

Boyce, M., Bryant, K.F., Jousse, C., Long, K., Harding, H.P., Scheuner, D., Kaufman, R.J., Ma, D., Coen, D.M., Ron, D., Yuan J. A selective inhibitor of eIF2alpha dephosphorylation protects cells from ER stress. *Science* 307: 935-939, 2005.

Bubber, P., Haroutunian, V., Fisch, G., Blass, J.P., Gibson, G.E. Mitochondrial abnormalities in Alzheimer brain: mechanistic implications. *Ann. Neurol.* 57: 695-703, 2005.

Budd, S.L., Nicholls, D.G. A reevaluation of the role of mitochondria in neuronal Ca^{2+} homeostasis. *J. Neurochem.* 66: 403- 411, 1996.

Butterfield, D.A. Elevated Glutathione as a Therapeutic Strategy in Alzheimer's Disease. *Drug Develop. Res.* 56: 428–437, 2002.

Cardoso, S.M., Santos, S., Swerdlow, R.H., Oliveira, C.R. Functional mitochondria are required for amyloid beta-mediated neurotoxicity. *FASEB J.* 15: 1439-1341, 2001.

Cardoso, S.M., Swerdlow, R.H., Oliveira, C.R. Induction of cytochrome c-mediated apoptosis by amyloid β 25-35 requires functional mitochondria. *Brain Res.* 931: 117-125, 2002.

Caspersen, C., Wang, N., Yao, J., Sosunov, A., Chen, X., Lustbader, J.W., Xu, H.W., Stern, D., McKhann, G., Yan, S.D. Mitochondrial Abeta: a potential focal point for neuronal metabolic dysfunction in Alzheimer's disease. *FASEB J.* 19: 2040-2041. 2005.

Chan, PH. Role of oxidants in ischemic brain damage. *Stroke* 27: 1124-1129, 1996.

Cheng, T.P., Reese, T.S. Polarized compartmentalization of organelles in growth cones from developing optic tectum. *J. Cell Biol.* 101: 1473–1480, 1985.

Cheung, H.H., Kelly, N.L,, Liston, P., Korneluk, R.G. Involvement of caspase-2 and caspase-9 in endoplasmic reticulum stress-induced apoptosis: a role for the IAPs. *Exp. Cell Res.* 312: 2347-2357, 2006.

Clapham, D.E. Calcium signaling. *Cell* 80: 259-268, 1995.

Cohen, F.E., Kelly, J.W. Therapeutic approaches to protein misfolding diseases. *Nature* 426: 905- 909, 2003.

Copanaki, E., Schurmann, T., Eckert, A., Leuner, K., Muller, W.E., Prehn, J.H., Kogel, D. The amyloid precursor protein potentiates CHOP induction and cell death in response to ER Ca(2+) depletion. Biochim. *Biophys. Acta.* 1773: 157-65, 2007.

Corbett, E.F., Michalak, M. Calcium, a signaling molecule in the endoplasmic reticulum? *Trends Biochem. Sci.* 25: 307–311, 2000.

Dailey, M.E. Bridgman, P.C. Dynamics of the endoplasmic reticulum and other membranous organelles in growth cones of cultured neurons. *J. Neurosci.* 9: 1897-1909, 1989.

Deitch, J.S., Banker, G.A. An electron microscopic analysis of hippocampal neurons developing in culture: early stages in the emergence of polarity. *J. Neurosci.* 13: 4301-4315, 1993.

Devaki, R, Shankar Rao, S., Nadgir, SM. The effect of lithium on the adrenoceptor-mediated second messenger system in the rat brain. *J. Psychiatry Neurosci.* 31: 246-52, 2006.

Dreher, D. Jornot, L., Junod, A.F. Effects of hypoxanthine-xanthine oxidase on Ca^{2+} stores and protein synthesis in human endothelial cells. *Circ. Res.* 76: 388-395. 1995.

Duchen, M.R. Mitochondria and calcium: from cell signalling to cell death. *J. Physiol.* 529: 57-68, 2000.

Ferreiro, E, Oliveira, C.R., Pereira, C. Involvement of endoplasmic reticulum Ca^{2+} release through ryanodine and inositol 1,4,5-triphosphate receptors in the neurotoxic effects induced by the amyloid-beta peptide. *J. Neurosci. Res.* 76: 872-880, 2004.

Ferreiro, E., Resende, R., Costa, R., Oliveira, C.R., Pereira, C.M.F. An endoplasmic-reticulum-specific apoptotic pathway is involved in prion and amyloid-beta peptides neurotoxicity. *Neurobiol. Dis.* 23: 669-678, 2006.

Ferri, K.F., Kroemer, G. Organelle-specific initiation of cell death pathways. *Nat. Cell Biol.* 3: E255-263, 2001.

Fischer, H, Koenig, U, Eckhart, L, Tschachler, E. Human caspase 12 has acquired deleterious mutations. *Biochem Biophys Res Commun.* 293: 722-726, 2002).

Finch E.A., Turner T.J., Goldin S.M. Calcium as a coagonist of inositol 1,4,5-trisphosphate-induced calcium release. *Science* 252: 443-446, 1991.

Floyd, R.A. Antioxidants, oxidative stress, and degenerative neurological disorders. *Proc. Soc. Exp. Biol. Med.* 222: 236-45, 1999.

Foyouzi-Youssefi, R., Arnaudeau, S., Borner, C., Kelley, W.L., Tschopp, J., Lew, D.P., Demaurex, N., Krause, K.H. Bcl-2 decreases the free Ca^{2+} concentration within the endoplasmic reticulum. *Proc. Natl. Acad. Sci. U.S.A.* 97: 5723-5728, 2000.

Frenguelli, B.G., Irving, A.J., Collingridge, G.L. Ca^{2+} stores and hippocampal synaptic plasticity. *Semin. Neurosci.* 8: 301-209, 1996.

Ghribi, O, Herman, MM, Pramoonjago, P, Spaulding, NK, Savory, J. GDNF regulates the A beta-induced endoplasmic reticulum stress response in rabbit hippocampus by inhibiting the activation of gadd 153 and the JNK and ERK kinases. *Neurobiol. Dis.* 16: 417-427, 2004.

Guo, Q., Sopher, B.L., Furukawa, K., Pham, D.G., Robinson, N., Martin, G.M., Mattson, M.P. Alzheimer's presenilin mutation sensitizes neural cells to apoptosis induced by trophic factor withdrawal and amyloid-peptide: involvement of calcium and oxyradicals. *J. Neurosci.* 17: 4212–4222, 1997.

Guo, Q., Sopher, B.L., Furukawa, K., Pham, D.G., Robinson, N., Martin, G.M., Mattson, M.P. Increased vulnerability of hippocampal neurons to excitotoxic necrosis in presenilin-1 mutant knock-in mice. *Nat. Med.* 5: 101-106, 1999a.

Guo, Q., Sebastian, L., Sopher, B.L., Mille,r M.W., Ware, C.B., Martin, G.M., Mattson, M.P. Increased vulnerability of hippocampal neurons from presenilin-1 mutant knock-in mice to amyloid beta peptide toxicity: central roles of superoxide production and caspase activation. *J. Neurochem.* 72: 1019-1029, 1999b.

Hampton, R.Y. IRE1: a role in UPREgulation of ER degradation. *Dev. Cell* 4: 144-146, 2003.

Hardingham, G.E., Arnold, F.J., Bading, H. Nuclear calcium signaling controls CREB-mediated gene expression triggered by synaptic activity. *Nat. Neurosci.* 4: 261-267, 2001.

Harding, H.P., Zhang, Y., Ron, D. Protein translation and folding are coupled by an endoplasmic-reticulum-resident kinase. *Nature* 397: 271-274, 1999.

Harding, H.P., Novoa, I., Zhang, Y., Zeng, H., Wek, R., Schapira, M., Ron, D. Regulated translation initiation controls stress-induced gene expression in mammalian cells. *Mol. Cell* 6: 1099-1108, 2000.

Harding, H.P., Zhang, Y., Zeng, H., Novoa, I., Lu, P.D., Calfon, M., Sadr, N., Yun, C., Popko, B., Paules, R., Stojdl, D.F., Bell, J.C., Hettmann, T., Leiden, J.M., Ron, D. An integrated stress response regulates amino acid metabolism and resistance to oxidative stress. *Mol. Cell* 11: 619-633, 2003.

Haze, K., Yoshida, H., Yanagi, H., Yura, T., Mori, K. Mammalian transcription factor ATF6 is synthesized as a transmembrane protein and activated by proteolysis in response to endoplasmic reticulum stress. *Mol. Biol. Cell* 10: 3787-3799, 1999.

He, Q., Lee, D., Rong, R., Yu, M., Luo, X., Klein, M., El-Deiry, W., Huang, Y., Hussain, A., Sheikh, M., Endoplasmic reticulum calcium pool depletion-induced apoptosis is coupled with activation of the death receptor 5 pathway. *Oncogene* 21: 2623-2633, 2002.

Heinitz, K., Beck, M., Schliebs, R., Perez-Polo, J.R. Toxicity mediated by soluble oligomers of beta-amyloid(1-42) on cholinergic SN56.B5.G4 cells. *J. Neurochem.* 98: 1930-1945, 2006.

Hetz, C., Russelakis-Carneiro, M., Maundrell, K., Castilla, J., Soto, C. Caspase-12 and endoplasmic reticulum stress mediate neurotoxicity of pathological prion protein. *EMBO J.* 22: 5435-5445, 2003.

Hitomi, J, Katayama, T, Eguchi, Y, Kudo, T, Taniguchi, M, Koyama, Y, Manabe, T, Yamagishi, S, Bando, Y, Imaizumi, K, Tsujimoto, Y, Tohyama, M. Involvement of caspase-4 in endoplasmic reticulum stress-induced apoptosis and Abeta-induced cell death. *J. Cell. Biol.* 165: 347-356, 2004.

Hoozemans, J.J.M., Veerhuis, R., Van Haastert, E.S., Rozemuller, J.M., Baas, F., Eikelenboom, P., Scheper. W. The unfolded protein response is activated in Alzheimer's disease. *Acta Neuropathol.* 110: 165-172, 2005.

Huang, H., Zhang, H., Ou, H., Chen, H., Gibson, G.E. α-Keto-β- methyl-n-valeric acid diminishes reactive oxygen species and alters endoplasmic reticulum Ca^{2+} stores. *Free. Radical Biol. Med.* 37: 1779–1789, 2004.

Iino, M. Biphasic Ca^{2+} dependence of inositol 1,4,5-trisphosphate Ca^{2+} release in smooth muscle cells of the guinea pig Taenia caeci. *J. Gen. Physiol.* 95: 1103-1122 1990.

Iwakoshi, N.N., Lee, A.H., Glimcher, L.H. The X-box binding protein-1 transcription factor is required for plasma cell differentiation and the unfolded protein response. *Immunol. Rev.* 194: 29-38, 2003.

Kanaseki, T, Ikeuchi, Y, Tashiro, Y. Rough surfaced smooth endoplasmic reticulum in rat and mouse cerebellar Purkinje cells visualized by quick-freezing techniques. *Cell Struct. Funct.* 23: 373–387, 1998.

Kaufman, R.J. Stress signaling from the lumen of the endoplasmic reticulum: coordination of gene transcriptional and translational controls. *Genes Dev.* 13: 1211-1233, 1999.

Kaufman, R.J. Orchestrating the unfolded protein response in health and disease. *J. Clin. Invest.* 110: 1389-1398, 2002.

Kudo, T., Okumura, M., Imaizumi, K., Araki, W., Morihara, T., Tanimukai, H., Kamagata, E., Tabuchi, N., Kimura, R., Kanayama, D., Fukumori, A., Tagami, S., Okochi, M., Kubo, M., Tanii, H., Tohyama, M., Tabira, T., Takeda, M. Altered localization of amyloid precursor protein under endoplasmic reticulum stress. *Biochem. Biophys. Res. Commun.* 344: 525-530, 2006.

Kuznetsov, G., Brostrom, M.A., Brostrom, C.O. Demonstration of a calcium requirement for secretory protein processing and export. Differential effects of calcium and dithiothreitol. *J. Biol. Chem.* 265: 3932–3939, 1992.

Lee, A.H., Iwakoshi, N.N., Glimcher, L.H. XBP-1 regulates a substet of endoplasmic reticulum resident chaperones genes in the unfolded protein response. *Mol. Cell Biol.* 23: 7448-7459, 2003.

Lei, K., Davis, R.J. JNK phosphorylation of Bim-related members of the Bcl2 family induces Bax-dependent apoptosis. *Proc. Natl. Acad. Sci. USA.* 100: 2432-2437, 2003.

Leissring, M.A., Akbari, Y., Fanger, C.M., Cahalan, M.D., Mattson, M.P., LaFerla, F.M. Capacitative calcium entry deficits and elevated luminal calcium content in mutant presenilin-1 knockin mice. *J. Cell Biol.* 149: 793-797, 2000.

Levesque, L, Annaert, W, Craessaerts, K, Mathews, PM, Seeger, M, Nixon, RA, Van Leuven, F, Gandy, S, Westaway, D, St George-Hyslop, P, De Strooper, B, Fraser, PE. Developmental expression of wild-type and mutant presenilin-1 in hippocampal neurons from transgenic mice: evidence for novel species-specific properties of human presenilin-1. *Mol. Med.* 5: 542–554, 1999.

Liu, C.Y., Schröder, M., Kaufman, R.J. Ligand-independent dimerization activates the stress response kinases IRE1 and PERK in the lumen of the endoplasmic reticulum. *J. Biol. Chem.* 275: 24881-24885, 2000.

Liu, C.Y., Wong, H.N., Schuaerte, J.A., Kaufman, R.J. The protein kinase/endoribonuclease IRE1α that signals the unfolded protein response has a luminal N-terminal ligand-independent dimerization domain. *J. Biol. Chem.* 277: 18346-18356, 2002.

Lodish, H.F., Kong, N., Wikstrom, L. Calcium is required for folding of newly made subunits of the asialoglycoprotein receptor within the endoplasmic reticulum. *J. Biol. Chem.* 267: 12753–12760, 1992.

Lu, P.D., Harding, H.P., Ron, D. Translation reinitiation at alternative open reading frames regulates gene expression in an integrated stress response. *J. Cell. Biol.* 167: 27-33, 2004.

Lustbader, J.W., Cirilli, M., Lin, C., Xu, H.W., Wu, H. et al. ABAD directly links Abeta to mitochondrial toxicity in Alzheimer's disease. *Science* 304: 448-451, 2004.

Marciniak, SJ, Yun, CY, Oyadomari, S, Novoa, I, Zhang, Y, Jungreis, R, Nagata, K, Harding, HP, Ron, D. CHOP induces death by promoting protein synthesis and oxidation in the stressed endoplasmic reticulum. *Genes Dev.* 18: 3066-3077, 2004.

Mattson M.P. Cellular actions of β-amyloid precursor protein and its soluble and fibrillogenic derivatives. *Physiol. Rev.* 77: 1081-1132, 1997.

Mattson, M.P., LaFerla, F.M., Chan, S.L., Leissring, M.A., Shepel, P.N., Geiger, J.D. Calcium signaling in the ER: its role in neuronal plasticity and neurodegenerative disorders. *Trends Neurosci.* 23: 222-229, 2000.

Mattson, M.P. Neurobiology: Ballads of a protein quartet. *Nature* 422: 385-387, 2003.

McCullough, K.D., Martindale, J.L., Klotz, L.O., Aw, T.Y., Holbrook, N.J. Gadd153 sensitizes cells to endoplasmic reticulum stress by down-regulation Bcl-2 and perturbing the cellular redox state. *Mol. Cell. Biol.* 21: 1249-1259. 2001.

Meldolesi, J., Pozzan, T. The endoplasmic reticulum Ca^{2+} store: a view from the lumen. *Trends Biochem. Sci.* 23: 10-14, 1998.

Michalak, M., Parker, J.M.R, Opas, M. Ca^{2+} signaling and calcium binding chaperones of the endoplasmic reticulum. *Cell Calcium* 32: 269-278, 2002.

Mori, K. Tripartite management of unfolded proteins in the endoplasmic reticulum. *Cell* 101: 451-454, 2000.

Nadanaka, S., Okada, T., Yoshida, H., Mori, K A role of disulfide bridges formed in the luminal domain of ATF6 in sensing endoplasmic reticulum stress. *Mol. Cell Biol.* 27: 1027-1043, 2007.

Nakagawa, T., Yuan, J. Cross-talk between two cysteine protease families: activation of caspase-12 by calpain in apoptosis. *J. Cell Biol.* 150: 887-894, 2000.

Nakagawa, T., Zhu, H., Morishima, N., Li, E., Xu, J., Yankner, B.A., Yuan, J. Caspase-12 mediates endoplasmic-reticulum-specific apoptosis and cytotoxicity by amyloid-β. *Nature* 403: 98-103, 2000.

Nakamura, T., Barbara, J.G., Nakamura, K., Ross, W.N. Synergistic release of Ca^{2+} from IP3-sensitive stores evoked by synaptic activation of mGluRs paired with backpropagating action potentials. *Neuron* 24: 727-737, 1999.

Niggli, E. Localized intracellular calcium signaling in muscle: calcium sparks and calcium quarks. *Annu. Rev. Physiol.* 61: 311-335, 1999.

Nishitoh, H., Matsuzawa, A., Tobiume, K., Saegusa, K., Takeda, K., Inoue, K., Hori, S., Kakizuka, A., Ichijo, H. ASK1 is essential for endoplasmic reticulum stress-induced neuronal cell death triggered by expanded polyglutamine repeats. *Genes Dev.* 16: 1345-1355, 2002.

Nutt, L.K., Chandra, J., Pataer, A., Fang, B., Roth, J.A., Swisher, S.G., O'Neil, R.G., McConkey, D.J. Bax-mediated Ca^{2+} mobilization promotes cytochrome c release during apoptosis. *J. Biol. Chem.* 277: 20301- 20308, 2002a .

Nutt, L.K., Pataer, A., Pahler, J., Fang, B., Roth, J., McConkey, D.J., Swisher, S.G. Bax and Bak promote apoptosis by modulating endoplasmic reticular and mitochondrial Ca^{2+} stores. *J. Biol. Chem.* 277: 9219-9225, 2002b.

Obeng, E.A., Boise, L.H. Caspase-12 and caspase-4 are not required for caspase-dependent endoplasmic reticulum stress-induced apoptosis. *J. Biol. Chem.* 280: 29578-29587, 2005.

Okada, T.K., Yoshida, R., Akazawa, M., Negishi, M., Mori, K. Distinct roles of activating transcription factor 6 (ATF6) and double-stranded RNA-activated protein kinase-like endoplasmic reticulum (PERK) in transcription during the mammalian unfolded protein response. *Biochem. J.* 366: 585-594, 2000.

Oyadomari, S., Mori, M. Roles of CHOP/GADD153 in endoplasmic reticulum stress. *Cell Death Differ.* 11: 381-389, 2004.

Padua, R.A. Yamamoto, T., Fyda, D., Sawchuk, M.A., Geiger, J.D., Nagy, J.I. Autoradiographic analysis of [³H]ryanodine binding sites in rat brain. Regional distribution and the effects of lesions on sites in the hippocampus. *J. Chem. Neuroanat.* 5: 63-73, 1992.

Padua, R.A., Nagy, J.L., Geiger, J.D. Subcellular localization of ryanodine receptors in rat brain. *Eur. J. Pharmacol.* 298: 185-189, 1996.

Pashen, W. Dependence of vital cell function on endoplasmic reticulum calcium levels: implications for the mechanisms underlying neuronal cell injury in different pathological states. *Cell Calcium* 29: 1-11, 2001.

Patil, C., Walter, P. Intracellular signaling from the endoplasmic reticulum to the nucleus: the unfolded protein response in yeast and mammals. *Curr. Opin. Cell Biol.* 13: 349-355, 2001.

Perlmutter, D.H. Chemical chaperone: a pharmacological strategy for disorders of protein folding and trafficking. *Ped. Res.* 52: 832- 836, 2002.

Pinton, P., Ferrari, D., Magalhaes, P., Schulze-Osthoff, K., Di Virgilio, F., Pozzan, T., Rizzuto, R. Reduced loading of intracellular Ca(2+) stores and downregulation of capacitative Ca(2+) influx in Bcl-2-overexpressing cells. *J. Cell Biol.* 148: 857-862, 2000.

Pozzan, T., Rizzuto, R., Volpe, P., Meldolesi, J. Molecular and cellular physiology of intracellular calcium stores. *Physiol. Rev.* 74: 595-636, 1994.

Putcha, G.V., Le, S., Frank, S., Besirli, C.G., Clark, K., Chu, B., Alix, S., Youle, R.J., LaMarche, A., Maroney, A.C., Johnson, E.M. Jr. JNK-mediated BIM phosphorylation potentiates BAX-dependent apoptosis. *Neuron* 38: 899–914, 2003.

Rao, R.V., Hermel, E., Castro-Obregon, S., del Rio, G., Ellerby, L.M., Ellerby, H.M., Bredesen, D.E. Coupling endoplasmic reticulum stress to the cell death program. Mechanism of caspase activation. *J. Biol. Chem.* 276: 33869-33874, 2001.

Racay, P., Kaplan, P., Lehotsky, J., Mezesova, V. Rabbit brain endoplasmic reticulum membranes as target for free radicals. Changes in Ca^{2+}-transport and protection by stobadine. Biochem. *Mol. Biol. Int.* 36: 569-577, 1995.

Reddy, P.H. Amyloid precursor protein-mediated free radicals and oxidative damage: implications for the development and progression of Alzheimer's disease. *J. Neurochem.* 96: 1-13, 2006.

Reddy, P.H., Beal, M.F. Are mitochondria critical in the pathogenesis of Alzheimer's disease? *Brain Res. Rev.* 49: 618-632. 2005.

Romisch, K. A cure for traffic jams: small molecule chaperones in the endoplasmic reticulum. *Traffic* 5: 815-820, 2004.

Rose, C.R., Konnerth, A. Stores not just for storage: intracellular calcium release and synaptic plasticity. *Neuron* 31: 519-22, 2001.

Rutkowski, D.T., Kaufman, R. J. A trip to the ER: coping with stress. *Trends in Cell Biol.* 14: 20-28, 2004.

Shacka, JJ, Roth, KA. Regulation of neuronal cell death and neurodegeneration by members of the Bcl-2 family: therapeutic implications. *Curr. Drugs Targets CNS Neurol. Disord.* 4: 25-39, 2005.

Schröder, M., Kaufman, R.J. ER stress and the unfolded protein response. *Mutat. Res.* 569: 29-63, 2005.

Scorrano, L., Oakes, S.A., Opferman, J.T., Cheng, E.H., Sorcinelli, M.D., Pozzan, T., Korsmeyer, S. J. BAX and BAK regulation of endoplasmic reticulum Ca^{2+}: a control Point for apoptosis. *Science* 300: 135-139, 2003.

Selkoe, D.J. Translating cell biology into therapeutic advances in Alzheimer's disease. *Nature* 399: A23–A31, 1999.

Selkoe, D.J. Alzheimer's Disease Is a Synaptic Failure. *Science* 298: 789-791, 2002.

Shamu, C.E., Walter, P. Oligomerization and phosphorylation of the Ire1p kinase during intracellular signalling from the endoplasmic reticulum to the nucleus. *EMBO J.* 15: 3028-3039, 1996.

Sharp, A.H., McPherson, P.S., Dawson, T.M., Aoki, C., Campbell, K., Snyder, S.H. Differential immunohistochemical localization of inositol 1,4,5 triphosphate- and ryanodine-sensitive Ca^{2+} release channels in rat brain. *J. Neurosci.* 13: 3051–3063. 1993.

Shen, Y., Ballar, P., Apostolou, A, Doong, H., Fang, S. ER stress differentially regulates the stabilities of ERAD ubiquitin ligases and their substrates. *Biochem. Biophys. Res. Commun.* 352: 919-924, 2007.

Shi, Y., Vattem, K.M., Sood, R., An, J., Liang, J., Stramm, L., Wek, R.C. Identification and characterization of pancreatic eukaryotic initiation factor 2 α-subunit kinase, PEK, involved in translational control. *Mol. Cell Biol.* 18: 7499-7509, 1998.

Shi, Y., An, J., Liang, J., Hayes, S.E., Sandusky, G.E., Stramm, L.E., Yang, N.N. Characterization of a mutant pancreatic eIF-2α kinase, PEK, and co-localization with somatostatin in islet delta cells. *J. Biol. Chem.* 274: 5723-5730, 1999.

Simakova, O., Arispe, N.J. Early and late cytotoxic effects of external application of the Alzheimer's Abeta result from the initial formation and function of Abeta ion channels. *Biochemistry* 45: 5907-5915, 2006.

Smith, IF, Hitt, B, Green, KN, Oddo, S, LaFerla, FM. Enhanced caffeine-induced Ca2+ release in the 3xTg-AD mouse model of Alzheimer's disease. *J. Neurochem.* 94: 1711-1718, 2005.

Sokka, A.L., Putkonen, N., Mudo, G., Pryazhnikov, E., Reijonen, S., Khiroug, L., Belluardo, N., Lindholm, D., Korhonen, L. Endoplasmic reticulum stress inhibition protects against excitotoxic neuronal injury in the rat brain. *J. Neurosci.* 27: 901-908, 2007.

Steiner, H., Haass, C. Intramembrane proteolysis by presenilins. *Nat. Rev. Mol. Cell Biol.* 1: 217-224, 2000.

Stutzmann, G.E., LaFerla, F.M., Parker, I. Ca^{2+} signaling in mouse cortical neurons studied by two-photon imaging and photoreleased inositol triphosphate. *J. Neurosci.* 23: 758-765, 2003.

Stutzmann, G.E., Caccamo, A., LaFerla, F.M., Parker, I. Dysregulated IP3 signaling in cortical neurons of knock-in mice expressing an Alzheimer's-linked mutation in presenilin1 results in exaggerated Ca^{2+} signals and altered membrane excitability. *J. Neurosci.* 24: 508-513, 2004.

Stutzmann, G.E., Smith, I., Caccamo, A., Oddo, S., Laferla, F.M., Parker, I. Enhanced ryanodine receptor recruitment contributes to Ca^{2+} disruptions in young, adult, and aged Alzheimer's disease mice. *J. Neurosci.* 26: 5180-5189, 2006.

Supnet, C., Grant, J., Kong, H., Westaway, D., Mayne, M. Amyloid-beta-(1-42) increases ryanodine receptor-3 expression and function in neurons of TgCRND8 mice. *J. Biol. Chem.* 281: 38440-38447, 2006.

Szalai, G., Krishnamurthy, R., Hajnoczky, G. Apoptosis driven by IP(3)-linked mitochondrial calcium signals. *EMBO J.* 18: 6349-6361, 1999.

Tardif, K.D., Waris, G., Siddiqui, A. Hepatitis C virus, ER stress, and oxidative stress. *Trends Microbiol.* 13: 159-163, 2005.

Tirasophon, W., Welihinda, A.A., Kaufman, R.J. A stress response pathway from the endoplasmic reticulum to the nucleus requires a novel bifunctional protein kinase/endoribonuclease (Ire1p) in mammalian cells. *Genes Dev.* 12: 1812-1824, 1998.

Urano, F., Wang, X., Bertolotti, A., Zhang, Y., Chung, P., Harding, H.P., Ron, D. Coupling of stress in the ER to activation of JNK protein kinases by transmembrane protein kinase IRE1. *Science* 287: 664-666, 2000.

Vattem, K.M., Wek, R.C. Reinitiation involving upstream ORFs regulates ATF4 mRNA translation in mammalian cells. *Proc. Natl. Acad. Sci. USA* 101: 11269-11274 2004 .

Verkhratsky, A., Petersen, O.H. The endoplasmic reticulum as an integrating signalling organelle: from neuronal signalling to neuronal death. *Eur. J. Pharmacol.* 447: 141-154, 2002.

Wang, J.F., Young, L.T. Regulation of molecular chaperone GRP78 by mood stabilizing drugs. *Clin. Neurosci. Res.* 4: 281-288, 2004.

Wang, X.Z., Harding, H.P., Zhang, Y., Jolicoeur, E.M., Kuroda, M., Ron, D. Cloning of mammalian Ire1 reveals diversity in the ER stress responses. *EMBO J.* 17: 5708-5717, 1998.

Wang, X.Z., Ron, D. Stress-induced phosphorylation and activation of the transcription factor CHOP (GADD153) by p38 MAP Kinase. *Science* 272: 1347-1349. 1996.

Wang, S., El-Deiry, W.S. Cytochrome c: a crosslink between the mitochondria and the endoplasmic reticulum in calcium-dependent apoptosis. *Cancer Biol. Ther.* 3: 44-46, 2004.

Welch, W.J. Role of quality control pathways in human diseases involving protein misfolding. *Semin. Cell Dev. Biol.* 15: 31-38, 2004.

Wisniewski, T., Ghiso, J., Frangione, B. Biology of Abeta amyloid in Alzheimer's disease. *Neurobiol Aging* 4: 313-328, 1997.

Wrzosek, A. Regulation of Ca^{2+} release from internal stores in cardiac and skeletal muscle. *Acta Biochim. Pol.* 47: 705-723, 2000.

Xu, C., Bailly-Maitre, B, Reed, J.C. Endoplasmic reticulum stress: cell life and death decisions. *Clin. Invest.* 115: 2656-2664, 2005.

Yankner, BA. New clues to Alzheimer's disease: unraveling the roles of amyloid and tau. *Nat. Med.* 2: 850-852, 1996.

Yamamoto, K., Ichijo, H., Korsmeyer, S.J. BCL-2 is phosphorylated and inactivated by an ASK1/Jun N-terminal protein kinase pathway normally activated at G(2)/M. *Mol. Cell. Biol.* 19: 8469-8478, 1999.

Ye, J., Rawson, R.B., Komuro, R; Chen, X; Dave, U.P.; Prywes, R.; Brown, M.S.; Goldstein, J.L. ER stress induces cleavage of membrane-bound ATF6 by the same proteases that process SREBPs. *Mol. Cell* 6: 1355-1364, 2000.

Yoneda, T., Imaizumi, K., Oono, K., Yui, D., Gomi, F., Katayama, T., Tohyama, M. Activation of caspase-12, an endoplasmic reticulum (ER) resident caspase, through tumor necrosis factor receptor-associated factor 2-dependent mechanisms in response to ER stress. *J. Biol. Chem.* 276: 13935-13940, 2001.

Yoshida, H.T., Okada, K., Haze, H., Yanagi, H., Yura, T., Mori, K. ATF6 activated by proteolysis directly binds in the presence of NF-Y (CBF) to the cis-acting element responsible for the mammalian unfolded protein response. *Mol. Cell Biol.* 20: 6755-6767, 2000.

Yoshida, H.T., Okada, K., Haze, H., Yanagi, H., Yura, T., Negishi, M., Mori, K. Endoplasmic reticulum-stress-induced formation of transcription factor complex ERSF including NF-Y (CBF) and activating transcription factors 6α and 6β that activates the mammalian unfolded protein response. *Mol. Cell Biol.* 21: 1239-1248, 2001.

Yoshida, H.T., Matsui, T, Hosokawa, N., Kaufman, R.J., Nagata, K., Mori, K A time-dependent phase shift in the mammalian unfolded protein response. *Dev. Cell* 4: 265-271, 2003.

Zhang, M., Yamazaki, T., Yazawa, M., Treves, S., Nishi, M., Murai, M., Shibata, E., Zorzato, F., Takeshima, H. Calumin, a novel Ca^{2+}-binding transmembrane protein on the endoplasmic reticulum. Cell Calcium: doi:10.1016/j.ceca.2006.11.009, 2007

Zhao, L., Ackerman, S.L. Endoplasmic reticulum stress in health and disease. Curr. Opin. *Cell Biol.* 18:444-452, 2006.

In: Cognitive Sciences at the Leading Edge
Editor: Miao-Kun Sun, pp. 87-96

ISBN: 978-1-60456-051-0
© 2008 Nova Science Publishers, Inc.

Chapter 7

THE P300 COMPONENT OF THE EVENT-RELATED BRAIN POTENTIAL AND BAYES' THEOREM

*Bruno Kopp**

Research Institute of Cognitive Neurology,
Klinikum Braunschweig and
University of Technology Carolo-Wilhelmina at
Braunschweig, Germany

ABSTRACT

The impact of the methodology of electroencephalography-based brain imaging on cognitive neuroscience has not been fully acknowledged yet. In particular, event-related brain potentials (ERPs) provide unique information to the study of the neural basis of human cognition. The article describes a Bayesian theory of the P300, perhaps the most studied ERP component. The theory was derived from several sources of knowledge. Firstly, empirical knowledge about factors that determine P300 amplitude and latency is considered. Here, the well recognized probability effect on the P300 proved to be the crucial factor. Secondly, Bayesian decision theory is shortly introduced. Recently, the conceptual framework of Bayesian statistics has been successfully applied to the sensorimotor system, and neuroscientific research on the Bayesian brain has just now been ignited. Thirdly, recent empirical knowledge about the neural basis of decision making is considered. A decision making model is shortly introduced because of its elegant simplicity, and due to the fact that it can be interpreted as a Bayesian decision maker. A Bayesian theory of the P300 arises from the integration of these different traces of knowledge, according to which P300 amplitude varies as function of Bayesian belief revision and P300 latency varies as a function of the duration of this revision process.

---

* Correspondence and requests for reprints: Research Institute of Cognitive Neurology, Klinikum Braunschweig and University of Technology Carolo-Wilhelmina at Braunschweig, Salzdahlumer Str. 90, 38126 Braunschweig, Germany E-mail: b.kopp@klinikum-braunschweig.de

The theory posits that the human brain codes and computes with probabilities, in a Bayesian manner, and that the P300 offers a window on the Bayesian brain.

Keywords: *P300, electroencephaolography (EEG), event-related potentials (ERPs), Bayes' theorem, probability, decision making, human brain.*

Electroencephalography (EEG) is widely adopted for the non-invasive assessment of cortical processing, mainly due to the high temporal resolution of EEG-based brain imaging. Developments in EEG acquisition technology and data processing capability have allowed for the identification and characterization of specific deflections comprising activities associated with given experimental stimuli or responses. These time-locked waveforms are identified as Event-Related Potentials (ERPs). The P300, first described by Sutton et al. (1965), is perhaps the most-studied ERP component, partly due to its relatively large amplitude and facile elicitation in experimental contexts. The P300 deflection emerges as a positivity, typically appearing approximately 300 to 500 ms following stimulus presentation. Timing of this component may range widely, however, from 250 ms and extending to 700 ms, with amplitude varying from +5 μV to +20 μV for auditory and visual ERPs.

Elicitation of the P300 may be achieved through an experimental *oddball* paradigm, in which subjects are exposed to a continuous succession of two types of stimuli, one presented regularly and the other displayed sporadically (Ritter and Vaughan, 1969). The P300 is elicited if an active classification task is added (Picton et al., 1995) in which each event belongs to one of two categories. For example, an experimental oddball paradigm may ask subjects to press a button when detecting male names (*target stimuli*) embedded in a sequence containing male and female names (Kutas et al., 1977). The cornerstone of P300 research is that its amplitude is inversely proportional to the probability of the eliciting stimulus category (*probability effect*) and that the P300 is larger to target than non-target stimuli at the same probability level (*target effect*; Duncan-Johnson and Donchin, 1977). Thus, a markedly increased P300 amplitude is usually observed in response to rare target stimuli of an oddball experimental paradigm. Other factors documented to alter P300 amplitude include stimulus sequence (Squires et al., 1976; Duncan-Johnson and Donchin, 1982), stimulus quality, attention, task difficulty and task relevance of the eliciting stimulus (for reviews see Linden, 2005; Luck, 2005; Nieuwenhuis et al., 2005; Picton 1992; Polich and Kok,1995; Soltani and Knight, 2000).

McCarthy and Donchin (1981) proposed that P300 latency varies as a function of factors governing stimulus evaluation time. As outlined above, the P300 amplitude is larger to infrequent stimuli, particularly when those stimuli are targets. Thus, the P300 must be generated after the stimulus has been categorized according to the rules of the task. This, in turn, implies that manipulations that postpone stimulus categorization (e.g., those that increase the time required for perceptual processing) must increase P300 latency, whereas its latency should not be dependent on post-categorization processes, such as response selection. However, the empirical issue whether or not the P300 is involved in processes that are related to response selection is still a matter of controversy (see Coles et al., 1995; Leuthold and Sommer, 1998).

Most well-characterized is the *P3b*, or "classical P3" (the term P300 refers to this P3b sub-component), with parietal topography. In oddball experimental paradigms, infrequent stimuli that are irrelevant to the task (distractors) but more salient than the targets, evoke the *novelty P3* or *P3a* (Courchesne et al., 1975; Squires et al., 1975), which peak earlier than the P3b and have a more frontocentral scalp distribution than the P3b. ERP waveform factor analyses indicate that the novelty P3 and P3a are identical, but that they are in fact dissociable from the P3b (Spencer et al., 2001). The P3a was conceived as a correlate of attentional orienting to salient distractors (Friedman et al., 2001), reflecting involuntary switching of attention to deviant events (Escera et al., 1998). However, evidence is accumulating which suggests that task irrelevance of a deviant stimulus is not an antecedent condition for eliciting the P3a (Debener et al., 2005; Kopp et al., 2006).

The P300 amplitude and Bayes' theorem were never linked together in a formal way, although the original article by Sutton et al. (1965) concluded that stimuli that "resolve the subject's uncertainty" elicit the P300, and despite the fact that the term *subjective probability* was continuously used to denote the functional significance of the P300 (e.g., Duncan-Johnson and Donchin, 1977). De Swart et al. (1981) cite some early, yet never persecuted Bayesian notions in the context of research on the P300. Friston (2005) repeatedly mentions the P300 in his Bayesian theory of cortical processing, but his article does not provide an explicit derivation of the Bayesian qualities of the P300.

Instead of that, the available evidence was summarized by theorists that the P300 is a cortical process supporting the formulation of an internal environmental model in which a stimulus needs to be evaluated. According to this "context-updating" theory (Donchin, 1981), the P300 is invoked in the service of *strategic* rather than *tactical* information processing. Whereas the tactical stream selects specific responses at any instance, the strategic stream is involved in the planning and control of behavior. Strategic processes comprise the long-term setting of priorities, the setting of biases, the deployment of attention, or the mapping of probabilities on the environment. In short, this stream is composed of a class of metacontrol processes which is concerned with maintaining a proper representation of the environment. According to an authoritative portrayal of the context-updating theory (Donchin and Coles, 1988), it "... asserts nothing more than that the P300 is elicited by processes associated with the maintenance of our model of the context of the environment" (p. 370). Alternatively, the "context-closure" theory (Verleger, 1988) emerged as an antagonist to context-updating theory, reflecting the concept that the P300 reflects activity of a memory trace remodelling post-detection of a target stimulus (Desmedt, 1980). However, these proposals were not followed by convincing lines of experiments providing support for them, probably due to the fact that the broad concepts of "context-updating" and "context-closure" do not specify how they are related to particular experimental manipulations (Luck, 2005).

Johnson (1984, 1986) proposed a triarchic theory of the P300 amplitude, according to which

$$\text{P300 amplitude} = f\{\,T \times [\,(\,1\,/\,P\,) + M\,]\,\} \tag{1}$$

with P = subjective probability (experimental variables affecting global stimulus probability, sequential expectancies), M = stimulus meaning (experimental variables affecting task complexity, stimulus complexity, stimulus value), T = transmitted stimulus information proportion of the total information received by the subject (with values between 0 and 1). Without going into the details of the triarchic theory here, it reminds us that the P300 amplitude is influenced by a variety of determinants. The purpose of this article is to provide a closer look at the *P*-factor of the triarchic theory of the P300 and to suggest that it possesses Bayesian qualities.

I start my line of reasoning with the statement that the interpretation, but not the mathematical properties, of probability is controversial. According to the "frequentist" interpretation, probabilities are merely limiting relative frequencies. However, in cognitive science applications, probabilities refer to "degrees of belief" or *subjective* probabilities (Gigerenzer and Murray, 1987). The subjective interpretation of probability generally aims to evaluate   conditional   probabilities, $P\ (h_j/d)$, that is (so-called inverse) probabilities of alternative hypotheses h_j about states of reality, given certain data, d, i.e. input available to the senses. Application of elementary rules of probability theory leads to Bayes' theorem (1763),

$$P\ (h_j/d) = [P\ (d/h_j)\ P\ (h_j)]\ /\ P\ (d) \tag{2}$$

In words, the components of Bayesian inference are $P\ (h_j)$ that reflects the prior belief in a   particular   state   before   the   sensory   information   is   received   and $P\ (d/h_j)$ that equals the *likelihood* of the sensory input given the hypothesized state. According to Bayes' theorem, the probability of the state given the sensory input, i.e. the *posterior P (h_j/d)*, is obtained by multiplying the prior by the likelihood and by normalizing the product (by scaling it so that the sum of the probabilities over all possible states sums to one). The posterior belief can then be used as the new prior belief for another perception, so that a belief can be updated within a series of perceptions sequentially through time.

Probability has only recently become a major focus of attention in the cognitive sciences. Indeed, classic work by Kahneman, Tversky and their colleagues (Kahneman et al., 1982; Kahneman and Tversky, 2000), but also earlier work (Phillips and Edwards, 1966), suggested that human cognition might be non-probabilistic in fundamental ways. Many of these studies may be best described as textbook probability reasoning experiments, and people are often poor at solving this kind of problems or "... fall victim to a range of probabilistic fallacies" (Chater et al., 2006, p. 288). But the fact that people seem to be poor probabilists is not in conflict with the hypothesis that aspects of cortical processing can be modeled in probabilistic terms. To use Chater et al.'s (2006) perspicuous example, the fact that Fourier analysis is hard to understand does not imply that it is not fundamental to perception.

The issue in probabilistic analyses of human cognition is to understand what is believed, or what can be inferred, about objects in the environment (Kersten et al., 2004), about regularities linking environmental objects (Tenenbaum et al., 2006), or about states of the motor system (Körding and Wolpert, 2006). Human visual perception is a subfield of cognitive science where Bayesian decision theory has been applied successfully (Geisler and Kersten, 2002; Kersten and Yuille, 2003; Stocker and Simoncelli, 2006). Von Helmholtz (1867) long ago regarded perceptions as being similar to predictive hypotheses and described visual perceptions as unconscious inferences from sensory data and knowledge derived from the past. Thus, the Bayesian decision theory mainly adds the probabilistic nature of the unconscious inferences to von Helmholtz' theory. The Bayesian theory of perception posits that perception is an unconscious process of probabilistic decision making. Perceptions are conceptualized as beliefs in hypotheses about states of reality, based on sensory evidence modifying subjective probabilities from previous experience, i.e. as evidence-based revision of subjective probability. Ultimately, these considerations lead to a Bayesian theory of cortical processing according to which the Bayesian brain represents information probabilistically, by coding and computing with probabilities (Friston, 2005; Knill and Pouget, 2004; Rao, 2005). A major challenge for cognitive neuroscientists is to test these ideas experimentally.

The neural mechanisms of perceptual decision making are only beginning to be understood although decision making plays a pivotal role in translating perception into action (Gold and Shadlen, 2001; Platt, 2002; Schall, 2001; Smith and Ratcliff, 2004). In perceptual decision making studies, single-unit recordings were obtained from monkeys that were trained to discriminate noisy visual stimuli and to report their perceptual decisions using eye movements. Neural substrates of perceptual decisions have been found in the frontal eye fields (FEF), the lateral intraparietal area (LIP), and the dorsolateral prefrontal cortex (DLPFC). The decision-related signals are usually considered to implement the decision transformation in these tasks, converting sensory representations into decision variables that evolve over time and that are capable of guiding behavior. The activity in these cells corresponds well with that of the behavioral eye movement decisions (Smith and Ratcliff, 2004). Thus, the temporal dynamics of the firing rates of neurons in the parietal and prefrontal cortex and of behavioral decisions have been described in parallel and they evidently converge.

In a general sense, neurons in sensorimotor structures accumulate evidence that leads to alternative categorizations (stimulus encoding), while other groups of neurons prepare and initiate overt responses (response preparation). Sequential sampling models (SSMs) are quantitative decision models that build on this fundamental distinction. According to SSMs, decisions are made by mechanisms that accumulate information to a response criterion (see Smith and Ratcliff, 2004, for a taxonomy of SSMs). SSMs have been successful in explaining behavioral data obtained from speeded decisions in perceptual and memory tasks (Ratcliff and Smith, 2004). As an example of a particularly economical SSM, Figure 1 illustrates the *LATER* model (*L*inear *A*pproach to *T*hreshold with *E*rgodic *R*ate; Carpenter and Williams, 1995; Sinha et al., 2006). According to the model, a decision signal S rises linearly at a rate r from a starting level S_0 until it reaches a threshold level S_T when a response is initiated. On different trials, r varies randomly in a Gaussian manner, resulting in a skewed distribution of response latencies.

Manipulations that lead to increases of the rate of rise r shorten response times, whereas any decrease of r prolongs response times. This empirically derived model is strengthened by its theoretical interpretation as a Bayesian decision maker. The decision signal S is identified with the perceived probability of the existence of a situation demanding a response. S_0 then corresponds to prior probability, r with the rate of arrival of sensory information, and S_T with a criterion posterior probability (Carpenter and Williams, 1995; Sinha et al., 2006).

The rest of this article introduces a Bayesian theory of the P300. Two hypotheses constitute the core of this theory. Firstly, the Bayesian theory of the P300 posits that

$$\text{P300 amplitude} = f \{ P (h_j/d) - P (h_j) \} \qquad (3)$$

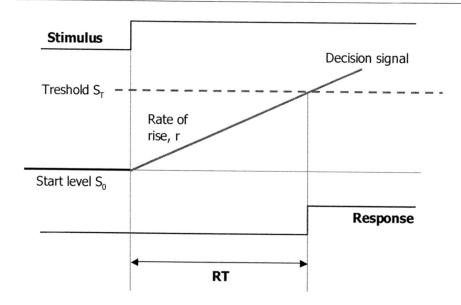

Figure 1. Illustration of the LATER model. A decision signal, initially S_0, starts to rise in response to a target stimulus of an experimental oddball paradigm at a constant rate r until it crosses a fixed threshold level, S_T. Response time (RT) is a function of the time at which the decision signal crosses S_T.

In words, P300 amplitude varies as a function of the difference between posterior probability and prior probability, i.e. as a function of the magnitude of evidence-based probability revision. Several basic empirical facts support the validity of the amplitude hypothesis of the Bayesian theory of the P300. To begin with, rare stimuli in experimental oddball paradigms elicit the P300 if and only if the processing of these stimuli involves task-relevant decision making (Picton et al., 1995). Most importantly, the probability effect on the P300 amplitude that was reported by Duncan-Johnson and Donchin (1977) and in an immense number of other oddball studies is also compatible with the amplitude hypothesis of the Bayesian theory of the P300. This holds true if one assumes (1) that subjective prior probability matches the relative frequency of stimuli and (2) that posterior probability is constant, i.e. that it does not vary as a function of the probability of stimuli. Figure 2 illustrates both assumptions. Inspection of Figure 2 reveals that at a given rate of rise r, P300 amplitude is inversely proportional to the probability of the eliciting stimulus (the probability effect). In contrast, even powerful manipulations of the rate of rise r should not affect P300 amplitude.

Secondly, the Bayesian theory of the P300 posits that

$$\text{P300 latency} = f \{ t(S_T) - t(S_0) \} \tag{4}$$

(t = time). In words, P300 latency varies as a function of the time interval between the starting level S_0 and the threshold level S_T. Inspection of Figure 2 reveals that at a given rate of rise r, P300 latency, akin to the P300 amplitude, is inversely proportional to the probability of the eliciting stimulus. In sharp contrast to what was predicted for the P300 amplitude, however, manipulations of the rate of rise r should strongly affect P300 latency.

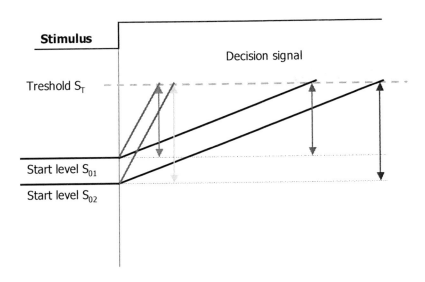

Figure 2. Illustration of the Bayesian theory of the P300. Target stimuli of an experimental oddball paradigm are presented at two relative frequencies, so that $S_{01} > S_{02}$. The probability effect on the amplitude of the P300 is identifiable as the length difference between the blue (turquoise) and the red (orange) arrows. Manipulations of the rate of rise r do not affect P300 amplitude, but they affect P300 latency.

It is important to notice that this Bayesian theory of the P300 is not primarily a theory about the P300. As outlined above, it is well recognized that P300 amplitude is controlled, in a multiplicative fashion, directly by the task relevance of the eliciting stimulus and inversely by the relative frequency of the stimulus (Johnson, 1984, 1986). Yet, the Bayesian theory of the P300 does not capture the basic interaction of the two factors that largely determine P300 amplitude (Picton et al., 1995) nor does it account for the target effect on P300 amplitude. Instead of that, the Bayesian theory of the P300 is an attempt to model the probability effect on P300 amplitude and latency, other things being equal. The theory adds some specific assumptions – that were derived from Bayes' theorem (Bayes, 1763) and from the LATER model (Carpenter and Williams, 1995; Sinha et al., 2006) – to the directly observable fact of the P300 probability effect. Its formulation thus reflects a cognitive theory about the kind of information processing performed by the human brain (Rösler, 1983). In particular, the Bayesian theory of the P300 posits that the human brain codes and computes with probabilities, in a Bayesian manner (Friston, 2005; Knill and Pouget, 2004; Rao, 2005). According to the theory, adequate research on the P300 offers a window on the Bayesian brain: Does the human cortex actually act like a Bayesian decision maker? The answer to this question is of great theoretical importance since it would help to shape valid theories about perception and cortical processing.

The major challenge for cognitive neuroscientists is to design the adequate experiment to test these ideas. Here, the fundamental problem is to comply with the ceteris paribus constraint. For example, manipulations of target probability in usual experimental oddball paradigms also change the absolute time between targets, i.e. the target-to-target time interval. Gonsalvez and colleagues have argued that target-to-target interval may better explain target-P300 amplitude modulation than target probability (e.g., Gonsalvez and Polich, 2002). Thus, the experiment designed to test the Bayesian theory of the P300 must dissolve the confound between target probability and target-to-target interval. These methodological subtleties notwithstanding, future P300 research will likely provide a window on the nature of the neural basis of decision making in the human brain.

ACKNOWLEDGMENTS

The research reported in this article was supported by the ZNS – Hannelore Kohl Stiftung.

REFERENCES

Bayes T. An essay towards solving a problem in the doctrine of chance. *Philos. Trans R. Soc* 53: 370-418, 1763.

Carpenter RHS, Williams MLL. Neural computation of log likelihood in the control of saccadic eye movements. *Nature* 377: 59-62, 1995.

Chater N, Tenenbaum JB, Yuille A. Probabilistic models of cognition: conceptual foundations. *Trends Cogn. Sci.* 10: 287-291, 2006.

Coles MGH, Smid HGOM, Scheffers MK, Otten LJ. Mental chronometry and the study of human information processing. In MD Rugg, MGH Coles (Eds.), *Electrophysiology of mind and brain* (pp. 86-131). Oxford, Oxford University Press. 1995.

Courchesne E, Hillyard SA, Galambos R. Stimulus novelty, task relevance and the visual evoked potential in man. *Electroencephalogr. Clin. Neurophysiol.* 39: 131-143, 1975.

Debener S, Makeig S, Delorme A, Engel AK. What is novel in the novelty oddball paradigm? Functional significance of the novelty P3 event-related potential as revealed by independent component analysis. *Brain Res. Cogn. Brain Res.* 22: 309–321, 2005.

Desmedt JE. P300 in serial tasks: an essential post-decision closure mechanism. *Prog. Brain Res.* 54: 682-686,1980.

De Swart JH, Kok A, Das-Smaal EA. P300 and uncertainty reduction in a concept-identification task. *Psychophysiology* 18: 619–629, 1981.

Donchin E. Surprise!...Surprise? *Psychophysiology* 18: 493–513, 1981.

Donchin E, Coles MGH. Is the P300 component a manifestation of context updating? *Behav. Brain Sci.* 11: 357-374,1988.

Duncan-Johnson CC, Donchin E. On quantifying surprise: the variation of eventrelated potentials with subjective probability. *Psychophysiology* 16: 53–55, 1977.

Duncan-Johnson CC, Donchin E. The P300 component of the event-related brain potential as an index of information processing. *Biol. Psychol.* 14: 1-52, 1982.

Escera C, Alho K, Winkler I, Näätänen R. Neural mechanisms of involuntary attention to acoustic novelty and change. *J. Cogn. Neurosci.* 10: 590-604, 1998.

Friedman D, Cycowicz YM, Gaeta H. The novelty P3: an event-related brain potential (ERP) sign of the brain's evaluation of novelty. *Neurosci. Biobehav. Rev.* 25: 355-373, 2001.

Friston K. A theory of cortical responses. *Philos. Trans. R. Soc. Lond. B. Biol. Sci.* 360: 815-836, 2005.

Geisler WS, Kersten D. Illusions, perception and Bayes. *Nat. Neurosci.* 5: 508-510, 2002.

Gigerenzer G, Murray DJ. *Cognition as intuitive statistics*. Hillsdale, NJ, Erlbaum. 1987.

Gold JI, Shadlen MN. Neural computations that underlie decisions about sensory stimuli. *Trends Cogn. Sci.* 5: 10-16, 2001.

Gonsalvez CL, Polich, J. P300 amplitude is determined by target-to-target interval. *Psychophysiology* 39: 388-396, 2002.

Johnson R Jr. P300: a model of the variables controlling its amplitude. *Ann. NY Acad. Sci.* 425: 223-229, 1984.

Johnson R Jr. A triarchic model of P300 amplitude. *Psychophysiology* 23: 367- 384, 1986.

Kahneman D, Slovic P, Tversky A. *Judgment under uncertainty: heuristics and biases.* New York, Cambridge University Press. 1982.

Kahneman D, Tversky A. *Choices, values, and frames.* New York, Cambridge University Press, 2000.

Kersten D, Mamassian P, Yuille A. Object perception as Bayesian inference. *Annu. Rev. Psychol.* 55: 271–304, 2004.

Kersten D, Yuille A. Bayesian models of object perception. *Curr. Opin. Neurobiol.* 13: 150-158, 2003.

Knill DC, Pouget A. The Bayesian brain: the role of uncertainty in neural coding and computation. *Trends Neurosci.* 27: 712-719, 2004.

Körding KP, Wolpert DM. Bayesian decision theory in sensorimotor control. *Trends Cogn. Sci.* 10: 319-326, 2006.

Kopp B, Tabeling S, Moschner C, Wessel K. Fractionating the neural mechanisms of cognitive control. *J. Cogn. Neurosci.* 18: 949-965, 2006.

Kutas M, McCarthy G, Donchin E. Augmenting mental chronometry: the P300 as a measure of stimulus evaluation time. *Science* 197: 792-795, 1977.

Leuthold H, Sommer W. Postperceptual effects and P300 latency. *Psychophysiology* 35: 34-46, 1998.

Linden DE. The P300: where in the brain is it produced and what does it tell us? *Neuroscientist* 11: 563-576, 2005.

Luck SJ. *An Introduction To The Event-Related Potential Technique.* Cambridge, MA, MIT Press. 2005.

McCarthy G, Donchin E. A metric for thought: a comparison of P300 latency and reaction time. *Science* 211: 77-80, 1981.

Nieuwenhuis S, Aston-Jones G, Cohen JD. Decision making, the P3, and the locus coeruleus-norepinephrine system. *Psychol. Bull.* 131: 510-532, 2005.

Phillips LD, Edwards W. Conservatism in a simple probability inference task. *J Exp. Psychol.* 72: 346-354, 1966.

Picton TW. The P300 wave of the human event-related potential. *J. Clin. Neurophysiol.* 9: 456-79,1992.

Picton TW, Lins OG, Scherg M. The recording and analysis of event-related potentials. In F Boller, J Grafman (Eds.), *Handbook of neuropsychology,* Vol. 10 (pp. 3-73). Amsterdam, Elsevier.1995.

Platt ML. Neural correlates of decisions. *Curr. Opin. Neurobiol.* 12: 141-148, 2002.

Polich J, Kok A. Cognitive and biological determinants of P300: an integrative review. *Biol. Psychol.* 41: 103-46, 1995.

Rao RP. Bayesian inference and attentional modulation in the visual cortex. *Neuroreport* 16: 1843-1848, 2005.

Ratcliff R, Smith PL. A comparison of sequential sampling models for two-choice reaction time. *Psychol. Rev.* 111: 333-367, 2004.

Ritter W, Vaughan HG Jr. Averaged evoked responses in vigilance and discrimination: a reassessment. *Science* 164: 326-328, 1969.

Rösler F. Endogenous ERPs and cognition: probes, prospects, and pitfalls in matching pieces of the mind-body puzzle. In AWK Gaillard, W Ritter (Eds.), *Tutorials in ERP-research: endogenous components* (pp. 9-36). Amsterdam, North-Holland. 1983.

Schall JD. Neural basis of deciding, choosing and acting. *Nat Rev Neurosci* 2: 33- 42, 2001.

Sinha N, Brown JTG, Carpenter RHS. Task switching as a two-stage decision process. *J. Neurophysiol.* 95: 3146-3153, 2006.

Smith PL, Ratcliff R. Psychology and neurobiology of simple decisions. *Trends Neurosci.* 27: 161-168, 2004.

Soltani M, Knight RT. Neural origins of the P300. *Crit. Rev. Neurobiol.* 14: 199-24, 2000.

Spencer KM, Dien J, Donchin E. Spatiotemporal analysis of the late ERP responses to deviant stimuli. *Psychophysiology* 38: 343-358, 2001.

Squires NK, Squires KC, Hillyard SA. Two varieties of long-latency positive waves evoked by unpredictable auditory stimuli in man. *Electroencephalogr. Clin. Neurophysiol.* 38: 387-401, 1975.

Squires KC, Wickens C, Squires NK, Donchin E. The effect of stimulus sequence on the waveform of the cortical event-related potential. *Science* 193: 1142- 1146, 1976.

Stocker AA, Simoncelli EP. Noise characteristics and prior expectations in human visual speed perception. *Nat. Neurosci.* 9: 578-585, 2006.

Sutton S, Braren M, Zubin J, John ER. Evoked-potential correlates of stimulus uncertainty. *Science* 150: 1187-1188,1965.

Tenenbaum J, Griffiths TL, Kemp C. Theory-based Bayesian models of inductive learning and reasoning. *Trends Cogn. Sci.* 10: 309-318, 2006.

Verleger R. Event-related potentials and cognition: A critique of the context updating hypothesis and an alternative interpretation of P3. *Behav. Brain Sci.* 11: 343-356, 1988.

von Helmholtz H. *Handbuch der Physiologischen Optik. Hamburg*, Voss. (1867).

In: Cognitive Sciences at the Leading Edge
Editor: Miao-Kun Sun, pp. 97-133

ISBN: 978-1-60456-051-0
© 2008 Nova Science Publishers, Inc.

Chapter 8

MEDIAL PREFRONTAL CORTEX AND PAVLOVIAN CONDITIONING

*D. A. Powell**

Shirley L. Buchanan Neuroscience Laboratory,
Dorn VA Medical Center, Columbia, SC 29209
Department of Psychology, University of South Carolina
Columbia, SC 29208
Department of Neuropsychiatry and Behavioral Science
University of South Carolina School of Medicine,
Columbia, SC 29208

ABSTRACT

The prefrontal cortex plays a central role in complex behaviors that require working memory, long term planning, appropriate response selection, etc. It has been known for some time that processing of emotional memories involves the medial prefrontal cortex (mPFC). Such emotional memories can be studied in animal models by using Pavlovian (classical) conditioning of autonomic adjustments. In the present review, papers reporting use of these techniques are first examined. It has now become apparent that, not only do learned autonomic responses involve mPFC control, but somatomotor Pavlovian conditioning also involves the mPFC. However, the conditions under which mPFC exerts control of somatomotor Pavlovian conditioning involve circumstances in which the conditions for acquisition of the response are not optimal, suggesting that prefrontal mechanisms are accessed only when higher level processing is required. Studies evaluating somatomotor conditioning, as a function of prefrontal involvement, are also reviewed, and a strategy for further understanding prefrontal control of these processes is outlined.

* Correspondence and requests for reprints: D.A. Powell, Ph.D., Shirley L. Buchanan Neuroscience Laboratory (151A), Wm. Jennings Bryan Dorn VA Medical Center, 6439 Garners Ferry Road, Columbia, SC 29209-1639, Phone: (803) 695-6821, FAX: (803) 695-7942, EMAIL donnie.powell@med.va.gov

ABBREVIATIONS:

Aβ	amyloid-beta peptide;
ABAD	Abeta-binding alcohol dehydrogenase;
AD	Alzheimer's disease;
AIF	apoptosis-inducing factor;
APP	amyloid precursor protein;
Ask1	Apoptosis-signal-regulating-kinase-1;
ATF4	activating transcription factor 4;
ATF6	activating transcription factor 6;
CICR	Ca^{2+}-induced Ca^{2+} release;
eIF2α	eukaryotic initiation factor-2 alpha;
ER	endoplasmic reticulum;
ERAD	ER-associated protein degradation;
GRP78	glucose-regulated protein 78;
InsP3R	inositol 1,4,5-triphosphate receptor;
IRE1	inositol requiring transmembrane kinase/endonuclease;
JNK	c-Jun N-terminal kinase;
PERK	RNA-dependent protein Kinase (PKR)-like ER membrane-localized kinase;
PS1	presenilin-1;
PS2	presenilin-2;
ROS	reactive oxygen species;
RyR	ryanodine receptor;
SERCA	sarco-endoplasmic reticulum ATPase;
TRAF2	TNF-associated factor 2;
UPR	Unfolded Protein Response.

1. INTRODUCTION

The prefrontal cortex (PFC) plays a central role in complex behaviors that require working memory, long-term planning, appropriate response selection, etc. (Damasio, 1994; Fuster, 1997). Consequently, it is also involved in wide range of neuropsychiatric disorders ranging from the degenerative diseases of old age (e.g., frontotemporal dementias, Alzheimer's Disease, Parkinson's Disease, etc.) to schizophrenia and posttraumatic stress disorders (see Goldman-Rakic and Selemon, 1997; Rauch and Shin, 1999). Prefrontal function has been studied in a variety of ways, using computational models (O'Reilly, 2006), animal models (Fuster, 1997; Powell, McLaughlin and Chachich, 2000), clinical material (Damasio, 1994), and more recently various brain scanning techniques (e.g., Buckner and Petersen, 1996). The primary objective of the present paper is to elucidate the role that medial prefrontal cortex (mPFC) plays in Pavlovian (classical) conditioning of autonomic and somatomotor responses. These Pavlovian conditioning models will first be briefly described. The next section will review research on the role of mPFC in conditioning of non-specific autonomic and somatomotor responses. A third section will review data implicating the medial prefrontal cortex in Pavlovian conditioning of specific somatomotor responses. A fourth section examines the role of the mPFC in extinction, and a final section summarizes the relevance of this basic research and its application to a specific model of mPFC function.

2. EXPERIMENTAL ANALYSIS OF PAVOLVIAN CONDITIONING

2.1. Specific and Non-Specific Responses

During Pavlovian, or classical conditioning, a signal, or conditioned stimulus (CS) consistently precedes an unconditioned stimulus (US). The US elicits an unconditioned reflex (UR) but as a result of pairings of the CS and US a conditioned response (CR) eventually occurs during the signal (CS), that in many cases resembles the original UR. The CR is thus a new or learned response, since it did not originally occur to the CS and is a response that is elicited by the CS/US contingency. This procedure is schematically illustrated in Figure 1.

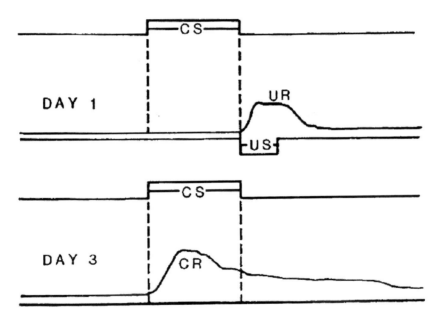

Figure 1. Polygraph tracing showing the topography of the unconditioned and conditioned eyeblink response as assessed during the first session of training (UR) and during the third session of training (CR). A .5 sec tone was the CS and the US was a 100 msec corneal airpuff.

In the rabbit eyeblink (EB) and nictitating membrane (NM) conditioning model, developed by Gormezano (1966), eyelid closure and nictitating membrane extension occurs as CRs to neutral conditioned stimuli (CSs), such as a tones, which systematically precede an airpuff or a brief periorbital electric shock train that serves as the US (see Figure 1). Note that the occurrence of the learned EB or NM response during the CS has no effect on the later occurrence of corneal airpuff or eyeshock reinforcer, as would be the case in operant conditioning. In the latter paradigm, occurrence of the CR would either prevent US occurrence or attenuate its magnitude (Gormezano and Coleman, 1973). This means that acquisition of the CR depends solely on the association between the CS and US, and not on any environmental effects CR occurrence may have. This type of learning is thus often referred to as "associative learning".

As has been noted by others (e.g., Schneiderman, 1972), when animals are exposed to classical conditioning contingencies that elicit a specific somatomotor response (e.g., EB or NM responses) a number of non-specific responses not usually assessed are concomitantly elicited. Although non-specific conditioned responses may also consist of somatomotor behaviors (Dykman et al, 1965) learned autonomic or visceral changes have been most often studied, including heart rate (HR), systemic blood pressure, skin conductance changes, etc. (see Obrist, 1981; Cohen and Randall, 1984; Smith and Devito, 1984; Weinberger and Diamond, 1987). It should be emphasized that the parametric features of Pavlovian conditioned somatomotor responses, which have been focus of most research on classical conditioning, and the concomitantly occurring non-specific visceral responses are very different (Powell et al, 2000). For example, the temporal parameters that are optimal for somatomotor and visceral conditioning may be quite dissimilar (Powell, Lipkin and Milligan, 1974; Schneiderman, 1972). Autonomic CRs are typically greatest in magnitude when the interval between the onset of the CS and US or interstimulus interval (ISI) is fairly long, e.g., from 4-8 secs (Powell and Kazis, 1976). However, little or no somatomotor conditioning occurs at these relatively long CS/US intervals. Rather the CS/US interval that produces the most rapid EB or NM conditioning is .5 sec or less (Schneiderman and Gormezano, 1964; Gormezano, 1972). A second striking difference between learned somatomotor and visceral responses is that the latter are acquired within just a few trials, usually ten trials or less, whereas many trials, up to 100, may be required before the first somatomotor CR occurs (see Lennartz and Weinberger, 1992, 1994; Kehoe and Mccrae, 1994 for a discussion of this issue when extremely long intersession intervals are employed).

Learned autonomic changes have been referred to as nonspecific responses, since they occur regardless of the nature of the conditioning contingencies (e.g., Powell, Buchanan and Gibbs, 1990; Prokasy, 1984; Weinberger and Diamond, 1987). Thus, signaled electric shock USs, delivered to either the orbital region or the foot pad of animals, results in a host of such non-specific CRs to the signal that are quite similar regardless of the site of application of the US. The learned somatomotor response in each case, however, is specific to the US, consisting of an EB CR in the former case and leg flexion CR in the latter case. Consequently, such responses are usually referred to as specific conditioned responses.

Figure 2 illustrates the dramatic differences observed in these two response systems in rabbits exposed to classical conditioning contingencies. It depicts the results of an experiment in which a 1216 Hz, 1 sec, 75 db tone was employed as the CS and a 250 msec, 3 mA, AC periorbital electric shock train was the US. The top panel of Figure 2 shows percent EB CRs over ten acquisition sessions consisting of 60 CS/US presentations each (conditioning group) and a single extinction session. A nonassociative control group received a random sequence of unpaired CS/US presentations (explicitly unpaired CS/US group). EB CRs increased from a low near-zero rate during session 1 to greater than 90% by session 10 in the conditioning group; the explicitly unpaired group showed virtually no EB responses.

The bottom panel of Figure 2 shows mean change in duration from pre-CS baseline of the third interbeat interval of the electrocardiogram following tone onset, as a function of acquisition sessions in the same two groups of animals. The third interbeat interval was chosen because it was the last one that was available for analysis in all animals before CS offset and the occurrence of the US. This interbeat interval usually represents the largest change from pre-CS baseline (Powell and Levine-Bryce, 1988). The duration of this interbeat interval, referred to as heart period, is the reciprocal of HR; as can be seen, it was lengthened by 5-10 msec as a result of training. Thus, HR CRs consisted of decelerations from pre-CS baseline. However, the heart period changes evoked by the tone in the unpaired group were much smaller and more variable, suggesting that the tone-evoked HR decelerations in the paired groups were associative. Note, however, that no acquisition function is apparent in the conditioning group, as was the case for the EB data above. The reason for this can be seen in Figure 3, which shows mean change in the third interbeat interval over trials during the initial session. In Figure 3, the acquisition function for heart period is clearly apparent. Change in heart period decreased in both groups across the first 3 to 5 trials, representing habituation of the decelerative cardiac component of the orienting reflex. The orienting reflex is the initial response to novel stimulation and normally also consists of bradycardia (Powell and Kazis, 1976). After habituation of the orienting reflex, the conditioning group demonstrated a second bradycardiac response of greater than 10-20 msec, whereas the unpaired group continued to show small and variable responses of 1-5 msec. Thus, the decelerative HR CR appeared by trial 5 and had reached its maximum magnitude by trial 10, well before EB CRs began to occur in any animal.

Plotting the HR change associated with the largest post-CS interbeat interval may, however, mask important temporal changes in the pattern of the HR CR. Thus, when beat x beat changes in CS-evoked HR change are plotted as a function of CS duration, a characteristic pattern of changes is observed. This pattern is shown in Figure 4, which shows the HR change from pre-CS baseline for 2 consecutive daily acquisition sessions, averaged over trials, as a function of post-CS interbeat intervals. The data are from eight rabbits that received differential HR conditioning using a more optimal 4 sec ISI (see Buchanan and Powell, 1989). There is an initial abrupt, but relatively small HR deceleration during the first, second, and sometimes third interbeat interval in response to both CS+ (reinforced) and CS- (not reinforced) presentations.

This HR deceleration becomes larger during subsequent interbeat intervals, increasing almost monotonically and reaching a maximum at tone termination when the US would be expected to occur. This regular pattern of the autonomic CR also occurs during human HR and skin conductance conditioning (Ohman, 1988) and has been recognized for some time. The initial small and short-duration component has been referred to as the "registration" or "orienting" component of the CR and the later-occurring and larger magnitude response has been referred to as the "contingency" component (Maxwell, Powell and Buchanan, 1994).

This characteristic shape of the HR CR not only has functional implications for the role of conditioned bradycardia with regard to behavior in general but also may be important for understanding the central nervous system (CNS) control of learned autonomic adjustments. For example, separate groups of neurons in the prefrontal cortex show differential CS-evoked changes during the contingency and registration components of the heart rate CR (Maxwell et al, 1994). A similar classification of neurons was also discovered in the mediodorsal nucleus of the thalamus, which is the thalamic projection nucleus to the prefrontal cortex (Chachich, Buchanan and Powell, 1997). These conditioned bradycardiac changes have also been shown to occur in a wide variety of Pavlovian conditioning situations, including the use of both visual and tactile CSs and in which either an air puff or sweetened water was used as the US (Powell, Gibbs, Maxwell and Levine-Bryce, 1993). The airpuff also elicits EB CRs, but the water is an appetitive CS which evokes jaw movements (JM) as skeletal CRs (see below).

Leg flexion conditioning in the rabbit is also accompanied by bradycardia (Powell and Lipkin, 1975). Learned HR decelerations thus appear to be a generalized phenomena of Pavlovian conditioning, regardless of the type of somatomotor CR. There is also some evidence that interference with the occurrence of this decelerative HR CR may adversely affect acquisition of specific EB CRs (Albiniak and Powell, 1980; Joseph and Powell, 1980; Kazis, Milligan and Powell, 1973; Powell, 1979).

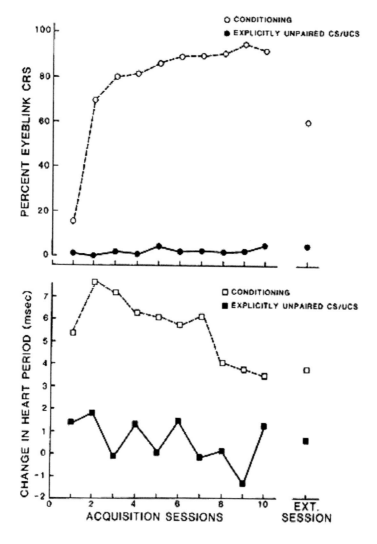

Figure 2. Top: Conditioned eyeblink responses of rabbits that received CS/US presentations (conditioning group) and rabbits that received explicitly unpaired CS/US presentations (explicitly unpaired group) as a function of ten 60-trial conditioning sessions. The CS was a 1 sec, 75 db, 1216 Hz tone that was followed by 250 msec, 3 mA, periorbital shock train. Bottom: Mean change in heart period from pre-CS baseline of the third post-CS interbeat interval of the same rabbits that received conditioning or explicitly unpaired CS/US presentations. The third interbeat interval is shown because it was the last one available for analysis in all animals prior to CS termination and is usually associated with the largest heart period change from pre-CS baseline. (From Powell et al, 1989).

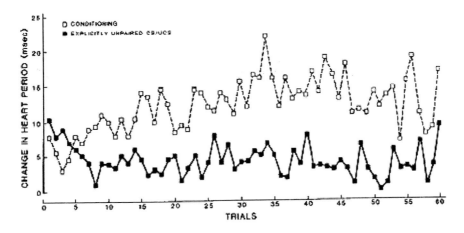

Figure 3. Change from pre-CS baseline in heart period of the third interbeat interval of rabbits that received Pavlovian eyeblink conditioning as indicated in Figure 2. The data are shown for conditioning and explicitly unpaired CS/US groups as a function of blocks of trials during the first session of training. (From Powell et al, 1989).

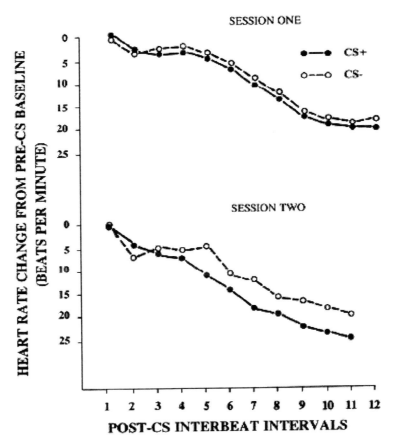

Figure 4. Heart rate change from pre-CS baseline in a group of 8 rabbits that received two sessions of differential conditioning in which either a 1216 Hz or 404 Hz, 75 db, 4.0 sec tone served as either CS+ (paired with US) or CS- (not paired with US). The data are shown in beats per minute, as a function of 12 interbeat intervals after the onset of the CS. (Adapted from Buchanan & Powell, 1989).

2.2. Theoretical Implications

The above-described results suggest that if Pavlovian HR and EB conditioning are both valid animal models of associative learning, they must represent different aspects of learning, since the parametric features of the stimuli required to elicit them and their rate of acquisition are different. Single process models of learning and memory thus may be inadequate to explain even simple associative learning phenomena, such as classical conditioning. This point has also been made by others (e.g., Lennartz and Weinberger, 1992). Indeed, it is well accepted that different aspects of learning and memory are related to underlying demands of the task being studied and the type of cognitive resources required (Kilstrom, 1987; Olton, 1979; Schacter, 1992; Squire, 1992; 1994; Tulving, 1985). These theoretical approaches to learning and memory have resulted in a typology of memory in which different kinds of learning and memory are used to accomplish different sets of goals. All of these models assume that different kinds of knowledge exist and therefore separate cognitive systems have evolved to deal with them, and moreover that different CNS mechanisms underlie the acquisition, storage and retrieval of these different kinds of knowledge (Squire, 1992).

Although memory systems have been characterized in a variety of ways by different theorists, considerable data support a model that includes at least two separate kinds of cognitive functioning. Squire (1992) has characterized these two kinds of processing as declarative and non-declarative. Declarative processing refers to information that is consciously retrieved, is dependent on intact hippocampal functioning, and, in many cases, is associated with a specific prior event (episode). This kind of learning thus refers to acquisition of facts regarding objects and relationships in one's environment as well as memory of the specific episodes during which these events occurred. By contrast, non-declarative memory involves acquisition of a) habits and skills, b) priming effects, c) learning of dispositions (including classical and operant conditioning), and d) non-associative effects such as habituation and sensitization (see Squire, 1992). Such learning may not necessarily occur at a conscious level and thus may not be associated with specific episodes in the past and, by implication, do not require hippocampal processing.

The separate acquisition functions and different stimulus parameters required for acquisition of the EB CR and other specific responses, such as the leg flexion or JM responses and non-specific visceral responses, such as the HR or skin conductance CRs, also tap different processes and therefore are dependent upon different CNS mechanisms. A six stage empirical model of somatomotor classical conditioning, depicted in Figure 5, reflects this idea.

It indicates a) the hypothetical constructs, b) behavioral correlates, and c) possible neuroanatomical structures associated with each stage. The six behavioral stages represented in this model are meant to describe the sequential events that take place when any mammalian organism is exposed to signals (i.e., CSs) that predict significant events (USs). However, the fact that the behavioral components of this model occur sequentially does not mean that the brain mechanisms or changes underlying these behaviors also occur in a sequential fashion. Indeed, it is highly likely that, depending on the type of paradigm being studied, parallel processing in different brain structures occurs simultaneously. Thus, the major point such a model is designed to make is that association-formation, as a result of exposure to classical conditioning contingencies, produces multiple memory traces involving both excitatory and inhibitory processes even at its simplest level. Such an analysis thus implies that multiple brain structures must be involved. It is now clear that this is the case. The brain structures listed in Figure 5, associated with these different stages of learning during classical conditioning, have varying degrees of experimental support, based on current evidence, as is discussed in more detail below.

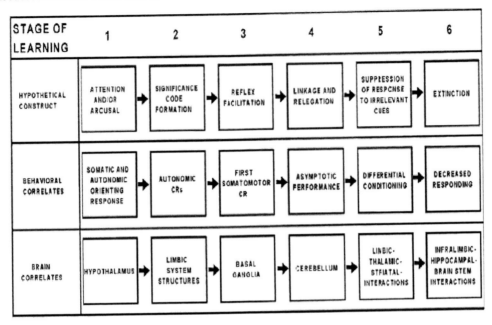

Figure 5. Diagram of a 6-stage model of classical conditioning, showing the hypothetical constructs, behavioral indices, and postulated neuroanatomical structures/mechanisms involved in each stage. The degree of experimental support for the latter varies depending upon the stage involved, but substantial evidence exists implicating the indicated structures in the behaviors listed in each case. Although the model suggests sequential processing in a step wise order, as noted in the text, some types of processing are almost certainly simultaneous and take place in a parallel distributed fashion.

2.3. Appetitive Classical Conditioning

The EB response system discussed thus far is a defensive reaction in response to an aversive US. Appetitive classical conditioning has also been studied in the rabbit using the JM response that occurs in response to presentation of water as the unconditioned stimulus. Appetitive Pavlovian conditioning training thus involves the repeated pairings of a tone (CS) and an intraoral injection of a 1 cc pulse of water (US) to rabbits that have limited access to water. A polygraph tracing illustrating the occurrence of EB and JM CRs and URs is illustrated in Figure 6.

The conditioned HR changes that accompany JM conditioning are illustrated in Figure 7. As this figure shows, the initial HR response during JM conditioning consists of bradycardia, but with continued training learned tachycardia begins to occur, as shown in Figure 8 which shows CS-elicited HR changes during JM conditioning over five consecutive daily sessions. As this figure shows, although CS-evoked HR slowing occurred during session 1, this response quickly began to become accelerative during sessions 2 and 3.

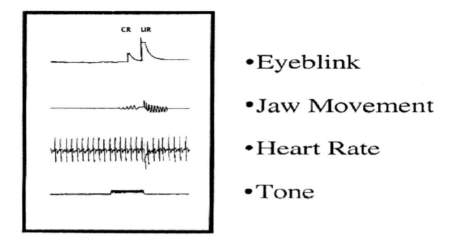

Figure 6. Polygraph tracing showing eyeblink and jaw movement conditioned responses (CR) and unconditioned responses (UR) to a tone conditioned stimulus. The accompanying ECG is illustrated for the JM response. Note the characteristic sinusoidal nature of the JM CR and UR as opposed to the discrete on/off character of the EB responses.

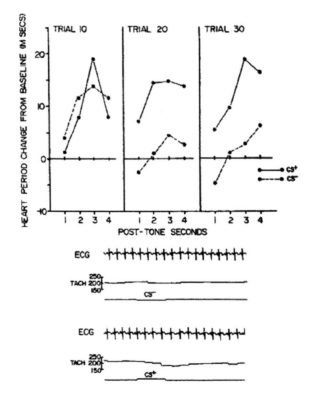

Figure 7. Top: Mean heart period (HP) change from pre-CS baseline during three nonreinforced test trials of rabbits that received 1-sec, 304- or 1216-Hz tones as CSs and a 1-ml pulse of water as a US. The US was systematically paired with the CS+ but never paired with the CS-. Data are shown as a function of four post-CS sec. Bottom: Polygraph tracing of typical cardiac response to appetitive CS+ and CS-. (ECG = electrocardiogram, Tach = tachometric equivalents of HR in beats per minute). (From Powell et al, 1993).

Heart Rate Responses During Each Session

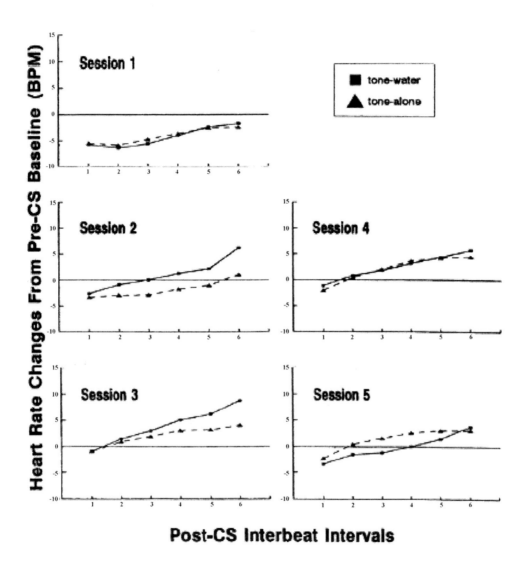

Figure 8. CS-evoked HR change in beats per minute (BPM) from pre-CS baseline, that occurred in response to a tone paired with water (tone-water) and a tone not paired with water (tone-alone), over five training sessions, as a function of six post-tone interbeat intervals (IBIs).

Of some interest in this regard is the question of why the cardiac changes accompanying appetitive conditioning consist of HR accelerations, while those accompanying defensive conditioning consist of cardiac decelerations. We know from earlier experiments that the latter response is primarily vagally controlled, although there is a small contribution produced by sympathetic inhibition (e.g., Kazis, Duncan and Powell, 1973). In order to determine the peripheral control of the learned tachycardia accompanying appetitive conditioning an experiment was conducted in which atenolol (a beta 1 receptor antagonist) and methylscopolamine (a peripheral vagal antagonist) were administered to rabbits undergoing JM conditioning (Powell, McLaughlin, Churchwell, Elgarico and Parker, 2002). The results of this study strongly suggest that the HR accelerations accompanying JM conditioning are produced by vagal inhibition. Thus, methylscopolamine abolished the conditioned tachycardia accompanying JM conditioning. However, atenolol, rather than attenuating this response, actually enhanced HR CR magnitude, which is also compatible with the suggestion that this response is totally controlled by vagal inhibition. These data are illustrated in Figure 9.

Interestingly, whereas vagal blockade with methylscopolamine decreased JM conditioning, atenolol actually facilitated it. These data thus suggest that although conditioned HR changes during appetitive and defensive conditioning are in opposite directions, they are both vagally controlled.

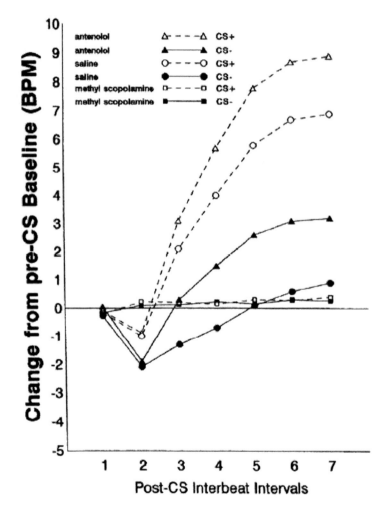

Figure 9. Mean heart rate change in beats per minute (BPM) from pre-CS (conditioned stimulus) baseline for groups of rabbits (n = 8 each) that received the peripheral autonomic antagonists as indicated. Data are presented as a function of 7 interbeat intervals that occurred during CS presentation. One acoustic stimulus served as CS+ and was always followed by water while another acoustic stimulus had no programmed consequences (CS-). (From Powell et al, 2002).

2.4. Fear Conditioning

A considerable amount of research has also been done, primarily in rodents, on what has come to be called "fear conditioning". In most of these experiments rats are exposed to a tone or light as a conditioned stimulus, which is paired with mild electric foot shock as a US. Under these conditions a variety of responses, which are usually referred to as "fear responses", are exhibited upon subsequent presentations of the CS. Typical fear indices have included a) freezing (or movement arrest, e.g. see LeDoux et al, 1986); b) enhancement of muscular reflexes (e.g., potentiated startle, e.g., see Davis, 1997); c) analgesia, or decreased pain sensitivity (e.g., see Fanselow, 1986); d) 22 Khz ultrasonic vocalizations (e.g., see Blanchard et al, 1991; Lee and Kim, 2004); and e) alterations in autonomic nervous system activities, as described in detail above. A critical review of Pavlovian fear conditioning has recently been published (Kim and Jung, 2006). Most of the evidence, as reviewed by Kim and Jung (2006), suggests that fear conditioning is mediated by the amygdala, although the mPFC also plays a role, as is described below.

3. MEDIAL PREFRONTAL CORTEX AND PAVLOVIAN CONDITIONING OF NON-SPECIFIC RESPONSES

The studies of Lofving (1961) in the cat and Kaada (1951) in primates, dogs and cats were the first to suggest that an anterior midline cortical region mediates a cardioinhibitory mechanism. Similar mechanisms exist not only in anterior cingulate cortex of the rabbit, but throughout the entire midline prefrontal region (Buchanan and Powell, 1982aandb; Buchanan, Valentine and Powell, 1985; Powell, Watson and Maxwell, 1994). This area is shown on diagrams of the rabbit's brain in Figure 10. The mPFC includes Brodmann's areas 8, 24, 25 and 32 in the rabbit. These areas, along with the more lateral insular PFC (PFCi; see Figure 10a), constitute the portions of the PFC from which bradycardia and depressor responses can be elicited by electrical stimulation (Buchanan, Thompson, Maxwell and Powell, 1994; Buchanan and Thompson, 1990; Powell et al, 1994). Moreover, lesions of mPFC greatly attenuate the bradycardia associated with classical conditioning, but damage to more lateral isocortex and insular PFC (PFCi) does not (Buchanan and Powell, 1982aandb; Chachich and Powell, 1999; Powell et al, 1994). Unconditioned cardiac responding to neither the CS nor US is affected by mPFC lesions (Buchanan and Powell, 1982a). Neuronal activity in the mPFC is also highly correlated with conditioned bradycardia, whereas that of the more lateral insular PFC is not (Gibbs and Powell, 1988, 1991; Gibbs, Prescott and Powell, 1992; Powell, Watson and Maxwell, 1994; also see below). mPFC lesions also eliminate the initial deceleration component of the HR CR during JM conditioning (see above), but have no effect on either the JM CR itself, or on the later-occurring conditioned tachycardia that accompanies JM conditioning. Thus, the mPFC appears to mediate the associative characteristics of inhibitory cardiovascular adjustments, a hypothesis supported by findings showing that functional anatomical pathways between the mPFC and brain stem cardiac control centers have been demonstrated in several species, including the rabbit (Buchanan, Thompson, Maxwell and Powell, 1994).

It has also been shown that the amygdala central nucleus (ACN) is involved in cardioinhibitory changes (Kapp, Frysinger, Gallagher and Hasleton, 1979; Kapp, Gallagher, Underwood and McNall and Whitehorn, 1982; Schwaber, Kapp, Higgins and Rapp, 1982). A host of other kinds of data also implicate the amygdala in learned emotional behaviors (see Adolphs, 1999; Bard and Mountcastle, 1948). The mPFC and ACN thus appear to exert parallel control over inhibitory cardiovascular adjustments, although reciprocal connections between the baso-lateral amygdala (ABL) and the mPFC have also been demonstrated (Buchanan and Powell, 1980; McDonald, 1991). In addition, considerable evidence also suggests that the plasticity associated with classical conditioning of autonomic changes may originate in structures in the primary sensory systems (LeDoux, 2000). Thus, autonomic CRs evoked by acoustic CSs are mediated by a pathway from the medial division of the medial geniculate nucleus (MGN) to the lateral nucleus of the amygdala (ALN) (LeDoux, 2000). Since the ALN also receives somatosensory input (LeDoux, Romanski and Xagoraris, 1989), it may be the site of the initial plasticity underlying "emotional" learning. The ALN projects to both the ACN and ABL nuclei, which projects in turn to the mPFC; thus the ALN could very well provide the plasticity associated with both mPFC and ACN control of conditioned bradycardia.

Another structure that participates in cardiac conditioning is the anterior cerebellar vermis. Cerebellar vermal lesions greatly attenuate HR conditioning in both rabbits and rats (Supple and Kapp, 1993; Supple and Leaton, 1990). It is not clear why removing only a portion of the autonomic brainstem inputs (i.e., prefrontal and amygdala inputs were still intact in these animals) should virtually abolish the response. Presumably, these different inputs control autonomic responding under varying stimulus conditions, but the exact nature of these conditions has not yet been determined.

The effects of medial prefrontal lesions have also been studied on fear conditioning. Morgan and LeDoux (1995) in rats and Voiuimba et al (2000) in mice found that lesions of the dorsomedial mPFC (area 32 or 24) enhanced fear reactivity by increasing freezing. However, most of the other work on the mPFC and fear conditioning has focused on the role of the mPFC in fear extinction. Morgan, Romanski and LeDoux (1993) first reported that mPFC lesions delayed fear extinction. However, these lesions were in the ventromedial PFC. i.e., infralimbic (area 25) or ventral prelimbic (area 32) cortex. Such lesions, however, had no effect on initial acquisition of freezing, indicating that the ventromedial PFC is specifically involved in extinction of the CS-induced fear response. However, Gewirtz, Falls and Davis (1997), using both pre- and post-conditioning lesions, found no difference between control and ventral mPFC lesioned rats in extinction, using both the freezing response and startle reflex as indices of the fear CR. Quirk, Russo, Barron and Lebron (2000) also reported that ventral mPFC lesions did not affect acquisition or within trial extinction of CS-induced freezing, but impaired recall of extinction on the next day. In summary, compatible with the data reviewed above, these studies suggest that the more dorsal aspects of the mPFC (i.e., areas 24 and 32) mediate acquisition of non-specific responses, while the ventral portions of area 32 and area 25 are involved in extinction. Thus, it seems clear that different mPFC areas are not only architectonically different, but have separate behavioral functions.

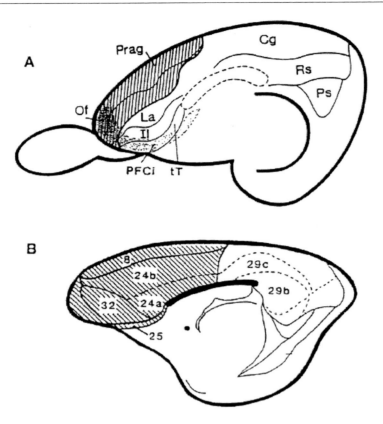

Figure 10. A: Schematic diagram of the rabbit brain, illustrating the structures in the prefrontal cortex from which cardioinhibition is elicited by electrical stimulation. The striped area indicates the portions of the midline PFC that have been demonstrated to be cardioactive, including all of the precentral agranula area (Prag) and the more dorsal portions of the anterior limbic area (La). Both of these relatively agranular (or dysgranular) prefrontal areas receive projections from the lateral mediodorsal nucleus of the thalamus (MDN), but this projection is much stronger to the more ventral anterior limbic area. The stippled area indicates a three dimensional representation of the lateral orbital and agranular insular areas (PFCi), which also receive projections from the thalamic mediodorsal nucleus, but these projections arise primarily from the medial MDN. Other abbreviations: Cg - posterior cingulate cortex; Re - retrosplenial cortex; Ps - post subicular area. This nomenclature is adapted from Rose and Woolsey [1948]. Note that it is somewhat different from that normally used to refer to the architectonic areas of the prefrontal cortex in the rat. B: Diagram of the medial aspect of the rabbit's brain showing the Brodmann numbers assigned to the medial prefrontal cortex based on an anatomical analysis by Vogt, Sikes, Swadlow and Weyland (1986). The striped area is that part of the prefrontal area which receives the projections of the mediodorsal nucleus of the thalamus and thus comprises the medial part of the agranular prefrontal cortex.

If the mPFC is a necessary CNS structure for the elaboration of conditioned non-specific adjustments, neuronal changes in this area of the brain should be evoked by classical conditioning contingencies. This appears to be the case, as described in several recent publications (Gibbs and Powell, 1988; Gibbs aand Powell, 1991; Gibbs, Prescott and Powell, 1992; Maxwell, Powell and Buchanan, 1994; McLaughlin, Powell and White, 2002; Powell and Ginsberg, 2005). An early study compared mPFC neuronal changes during EB and HR conditioning, using eyeshock as the US in one group of subjects, and airpuff as the US, in a second group (Powell, Maxwell and Penney, 1996). Although EB and NM conditioning occurred in both groups, HR conditioning was not significantly different from a pseudoconditioning control group when the airpuff was the US. Moreover, CS-evoked multiple unit activity (MUA) was considerably greater in the eyeshock than airpuff group, suggesting that the mPFC neuronal discharge associated with classical conditioning may indeed be in support of an emotional component of behavior, assuming that eyeshock is a more aversive US than the airpuff. In addition, recent findings that mPFC lesions attenuate the facilitation of the EB UR produced by Pavlovian conditioning, but have no effect on prepulse inhibition of the EB UR support this contention (McLaughlin, Flaten, Chachich and Powell, 2001), since conditioned EB reflex modification has an affective component, while prepulse inhibition does not (e.g., see Ison and Hoffman, 1983).

Later studies have focused on single unit activity in the mPFC during HR conditioning (Gibbs and Powell, 1988, 1991; Gibbs et al, 1992; Maxwell et al, 1994; McLaughlin et al, 2002; Powell and Ginsberg, 2005). These studies all show that both CS-evoked excitatory and inhibitory discharge occurs in the neurons in the mPFC, although some biphasic cells were observed as well. Of some concern in these electrophysiological studies has been the question of whether these CS-evoked changes originate in the mPFC or reflect the action of peripheral end-organ activity carried to forebrain areas by autonomic afferents. It has been known for some time that vagal, as well as sympathetic afferents, reach both areas 24 and 32 of the mPFC (Newman, 1974). A recently completed series of studies (Powell and Ginsberg, 2005) examined this question by studying HR conditioning and associated mPFC single unit activity in animals that were administered atenolol (a peripheral adrenergic beta blockade) or methylscopolamine (peripheral vagal blockade). Unit activity under these conditions was compared to the discharge of the same cells during vehicle sessions. Neither spike amplitude nor CS-evoked activity of over 84 cells was affected by peripheral autonomic blockade, suggesting that this activity is centrally initiated in the mPFC and not the result of peripheral afferent feedback.

Another important aspect of this study was the finding that the discharge of a subset of these cells showed trial-related changes in discharge that was related to acquisition of the HR discrimination between a reinforced CS+ that was paired with the US and non-reinforced CS- that was not. It was not possible in previous studies to draw this conclusion, since recordings in these structures were made during extinction after training was complete. In these studies recordings were made from a stiff fixed electrode that was acutely lowered into the brain. Data collection during extinction was necessary, because it is difficult to record from a single cell over successive trials during acquisition using this procedure due to head movements produced by the presentation of the eyeshock US. However, in a more recent study (i.e., Powell and Ginsberg, 2005), chronic recording of multiunit activity was accomplished via fine wires resting in the brain. Off line separation of single units from such activity can then be obtained over trials so that single cell activity can be associated with the acquisition of the behavioral CR (i.e., the CS-evoked HR changes). This study showed that a subset of mPFC cells show trial-related changes in discharge that were related to the magnitude of the HR CR.

Neurophysiological recording studies also point toward the involvement of the mPFC in fear conditioning and extinction. Milad and Quirk (2002), for example, showed that neurons in the infralimbic cortex were related to extinction memory. Although these cells were not responsive to the CS during conditioning or on the first day of extinction, they showed significant increases in response to CS presentations on day 2 of extinction, suggesting that these cells signal memory for extinction. Moreover, Quirk et al (2000) found that infralimbic stimulation paired with the CS reduced freezing and accelerated extinction learning.

Consequently, it can be concluded from these studies that the dorsomedial mPFC, including areas 32 and 24, are involved in acquisition of fear conditioning, but more ventral prelimbic and infralimbic cortex appear to be involved in extinction. These electrophysiological results are thus compatible with the lesion results discussed previously.

4. MEDIAL PREFRONTAL CORTEX AND PAVLOVIAN CONDITIONING OF SPECIFIC SOMATOMOTOR RESPONSES

4.1. Delay Versus Trace Conditioning

An essential neural substrate for somatomotor, i.e., EB, NM, and leg flexion, conditioning appears to exist in extrapyramidal cerebellar and pontine structures (Thompson, 2005). Lesions of the deep nuclei of the cerebellum and/or perhaps the cerebellar cortex completely prevent EB or NM conditioning from occurring in the ipsilateral eye, without affecting the UR (Thompson, 2005). Damage to the substantia nigra and caudate nucleus also retards, but does not abolish, acquisition of the EB CR (Kao and Powell, 1988; Powell, Mankowski and Buchanan, 1978). However, neither cerebellar nor nigrostriatal lesions affect HR conditioning (Kao and Powell, 1988; Lavond, Lincoln, McCormick and Thompson, 1984; Powell et al, 1978). A variety of other kinds of evidence (e.g., electrophysiological changes) strongly support the contention that an essential neural substrate for somatomotor learning exists in extrapyramidal structures (Thompson, 2005).

It is clear then that separate substrates mediate autonomic and somatomotor conditioning; i.e., much evidence, as reviewed above, suggests that corticolimbic structures mediate learned autonomic adjustments but cerebellar and neostriatal structures mediate somatomotor learning. However, there are interconnections between these two systems, especially in the PFC, providing for possible functional interactions between them (e.g., see Buchanan, Thompson, Maxwell and Powell, 1994; Powell et al, 1990; Powell, McLaughlin and Chachich, 2000). Cortico-limbic structures, including the amygdala, hippocampus and mPFC may also at least partially determine somatomotor response acquisition, even though the essential neural substrate for acquisition and expression of this response is in the cerebellum. Much of the evidence for this model of classical conditioning comes from studies showing impairments of EB conditioning by hippocampectomy in the trace, but not simple, delay conditioning paradigms (Maxwell, Powell and Buchanan, 1994; Reiman, Lane, Ahern, Schwartz and Davidson and Nadel, 2000).

The difference between delay and trace conditioning is schematically illustrated in Figure 11. In the trace paradigm (bottom) there is a brief temporal gap between the termination of the CS and onset of the US. This procedure can be contrasted with the normal delay procedure (top), in which the CS and US either overlap and co-terminate, or US onset occurs simultaneously with CS termination. Acquisition is normally slower using the trace paradigm, and hippocampal lesions differentially impair acquisition during trace conditioning (Weiss and Disterhoft, 1996), but have no effect on or may actually facilitate acquisition in the delay paradigm (see Thompson, 2005 for a recent review). Although the mechanisms for these effects are not clearly understood, it is assumed by most that under ideal conditions, i.e., when the conditioning parameters are optimal for acquisition of the response (i.e., during delay conditioning with relatively short ISIs), limbic system input from the hippocampus and other structures (e.g., mPFC) is not necessary for the memory trace to be carried through the interstimulus interval. However, during trace procedures, in which the CS is not physically present to activate appropriate memory mechanisms, cortico-limbic input to extrapyramidal structures is necessary for the memory to persist through the trace period (Weiss and Disterhoft, 1996). It is possible that the neural substrate for this kind of interaction between extrapyramidal and cortico-limbic structures is through the efferent projections from the PFC to the striatum and possibly pons (e.g., Groenewegen, Berendse and Haber, 1993; Mogensen, Ciriello, Garland and Wu, 1987). Cerebellar inputs to the PFC via the thalamus have also been demonstrated (Middleton and Strick, 1994). A cerebellar-striatal-thalamic-PFC module that controls associative learning is thus a possibility, as has been suggested by others (Houk and Wise, 1995; Weiss and Disterhoft, 1996). Such models suggest that classical conditioning involves multiple distributed brain structures, as discussed in detail above.

CONDITIONING PARADIGMS

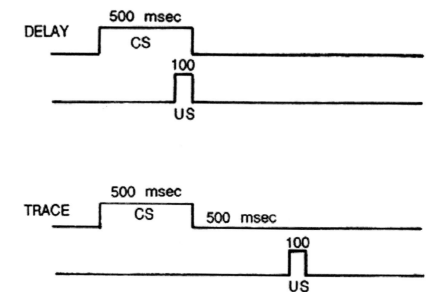

Figure 11. Schematic diagram of delay and trace conditioning. The top two traces illustrate the presentation of a 500 msec conditioned stimulus (CS) which overlaps and coterminates with a 100 msec unconditioned stimulus (US). The bottom two tracings show a 500 msec CS separated from the 100 msec unconditioned stimulus by a 500 msec trace period.

Also supporting such a model are findings showing that EB CR acquisition using other less-than-optimal paradigms is affected by damage to cortico-limbic structures. For example, hippocampal lesions also impair EB performance in discrimination/reversal paradigms (Buchanan and Powell, 1980; Powell and Buchanan, 1980). In this paradigm one CS (CS+) is followed by the US (e.g., an airpuff or periorbital shock) and another CS (CS-) is not; the reversal procedure involves switching the CS+ and CS- after a discrimination between them is attained so that the original CS+ becomes the CS- and vice versa. Typically, in animals with hippocampal lesions, mild impairments in the original differentiation between the CS+

and CS- are obtained, but severe reversal impairments are observed (Buchanan and Powell, 1980). Impairments in a discrimination/reversal paradigm have also been demonstrated subsequent to damage to the mediodorsal nucleus (MDN) of the thalamus, which provides the specific thalamic projections to the mPFC, (Buchanan, 1991). Similar impairments as a result of mPFC damage have also recently been reported (Chachich and Powell, 2004) It was also recently found that damage to the MDN produces a dramatic effect on EB conditioning when other parameters are less than optimal for acquisition, such as when reinforcement schedules are extremely lean (Buchanan, Penney, Tebbutt and Powell, 1997) or when the ISI is longer than is optimal. However, only modest lesion effects are obtained when optimal parameters are employed.

These kinds of findings suggest that although separate substrates mediate the autonomic and somatomotor components of associative learning, there are interactions between them, when conditions are not optimal for acquisition. A series of studies of EB conditioning in human subjects, reported by Squire and colleagues (Clark and Squire, 1998; Clark, Manns and Squire, 2001; Manns, Clark and Squire, 2000) reinforces this conclusion. In a first study, four human subjects with amnesia due to midline diencephalic (viz. hippocampal and/or thalamic) damage, were compared to normal controls on both delay and trace differential conditioning. The amnesic patients showed little evidence of EB conditioning on a trace task with a 250 ms CS and a 1000 ms trace period, but showed normal conditioning on a delay task with a 1000 ms interstimulus interval. Even more interesting, a post-experimental true-false test, designed to determine the extent of the subjects' "conscious awareness" of the experimental contingencies, showed that none of the 4 brain damaged subjects were "aware" of these contingencies. Moreover, several normal subjects also failed to show trace conditioning and were also "unaware" of the contingencies, whereas normal subjects that acquired the trace EB CR were all able to verbalize the contingences, based on the post-experimental test. Both "aware" and "non-aware" normal subjects, however, acquired the delay EB CR. These findings led the authors to conclude that perhaps EB trace conditioning should be classified as a declarative task, since it depends both on "conscious awareness" of the experimental contingencies and intact hippocampal functioning, whereas delay conditioning is non-declarative (viz. procedural), since it was normally acquired by all subjects whether "aware" or "unaware". More importantly, brain damaged subjects acquired delay conditioning normally.

Further, Daum and colleagues have shown that patients with temporal lobe lesions are impaired on a conditioned discrimination task in which a visual stimulus served as a signal for the occurrence of an auditory stimulus that signaled a corneal airpuff (Daum, Channon, Polkey and Gray, 1991), but showed normal acquisition, compared to non-brain damaged controls, on an EB simple discrimination task (Daum, Channon and Gray, 1992). Gabrieli, McGlinchey-Berroth, Carrilo, Gluck, Cermak and Disterhoft (1995) also reported intact delay EB conditioning in amnesic patients, whereas this same group reported impaired trace EB conditioning in temporal lobe damaged amnesic patients (McGlinchey-Berroth, Carrillo, Gabrieli, Braun and Disterhoft, 1997). Several reports, however, have indicated that human subjects with cerebellar damage fail to show normal delay EB conditioning (Daum, Schugens, Ackerman, Lutzenberger, Dichgans and Birbaumer, 1993; Solomon, Stowe and Pendleberry, 1989; Topka, Valls-Sole, Massaquoi and Hallett, 1993), reinforcing the conclusion based on animal studies, described above, that cerebellar structures are necessary for delay EB conditioning.

All human studies reported so far thus support conclusions drawn from non-human animals; viz. that cortico-limbic damage has no effect on EB conditioning using optimal delay conditioning parameters, but severely impairs conditioning when these parameters are not optimal, as during a conditioned discrimination paradigm or during trace conditioning. On the other hand, cerebellar damage impairs both delay and trace conditioning, even under optimal circumstances. These findings thus clearly support the conclusion that simple delay conditioning comprises a non-declarative task, whereas other kinds of EB conditioning may be classified as declarative, based on Squire's definition of these two types of learning and memory (Squire, 2002).

4.2. Studies of Trace Eyeblink Conditioning in Rabbits

As described above, several studies have shown that damage to the hippocampus impairs trace, but not delay EB conditioning in the rabbit (James, Hardiman and Yeo, 1987; Moyer, Deyo and Disterhoft, 1990; Port et al, 1986). Moreover, Chachich, Penney and Powell (1996) showed retrograde labeling of efferents to the mPFC in the dorsal but not ventral subiculum or CA1 or CA2 cells of the hippocampus proper in the rabbit. This experiment thus showed that the PFC of the rabbit, like the rat, cat and primate, receives information based on hippocampal processing. These findings lead to the supposition that prefrontal processing, as a result of hippocampal input, might also be related to somatomotor classical conditioning under non-optimal conditions. Indeed, Disterhoft and colleagues have shown that damage to more posterior mPFC results in deficits in the trace but not delay EB conditioned response in the rabbit (Kronforst-Collins and Disterhoft, 1998; Weible, McEchron and Disterhoft, 2000). However, attempts to replicate these findings have not met with total success. Using similar CS durations to that of Kronforst-Collins and Disterhoft (1998), who used a 100 msec CS, and Weible et al (2000), who used a 250 msec CS, McLaughlin, Skaggs, Churchwell and Powell (2002) were not able to demonstrate deficits in trace EB conditioning as a result of mPFC damage. However, extending the CS duration to 500 msec resulted in trace but not delay conditioning deficits.

Later experiments have shown that a critical variable in studies of mPFC control of trace EB conditioning is the type of US employed (i.e., eyeshock or airpuff). For example, Oswald, Knuckley, Mahan, Sanders and Powell (2006) compared groups of rabbits with mPFC lesions or sham lesions, half of which were subjected to a periorbital shock US and half a corneal airpuff US. Using a short CS duration (300 msec), similar to that employed in the original Disterhoft studies, these investigators found that, although conditioning deficits were obtained in the animals that received the corneal airpuff US, these deficits were not observed in animals that were administered the periorbital shock US (Oswald et al, 2006). As noted, however, McLaughlin et al (2002) obtained mPFC-produced deficits in lesioned animals in which eyeshock was the US using a longer 500 msec CS duration. A later experiment thus compared periorbital shock and corneal airpuff in groups of rabbits that received sham or mPFC lesions, but in which both the CS and trace duration was 500 msec. Only thirty acquisition trials were employed, with a 1 min average intertrial interval (ITI), since longer ITIs result in faster learning (e.g., Prokasy, Grant and Myers, 1958). Even when utilizing these extremely optimal learning parameters, however, large differences in EB conditioning performance between animals given periorbital shock and airpuff USs occurred; i.e., lesion induced acquisition reductions were much greater using the corneal airpuff than the periorbital shock US, although the differences between the sham and lesioned groups were statistically significant in both instances. Differences between the shock and airpuff groups were also highly significant (p<.0001). In this experiment a pseudoconditioning control group was also employed in which random unpaired presentations of tone and shock occurred. Both lesion and sham groups that received periorbital shock as the US showed significantly higher percent EB CRs than the unpaired groups. Although EB CRs of the sham-airpuff group were also greater than that of the unpaired control group, percent EB CRs of the lesion-airpuff group were not. This finding thus suggests that associative learning failed to occur in the mPFC lesioned animals that received the relative unaversive airpuff US. Consequently, it is clear that mPFC damage retards trace EB conditioning, but its effects are more severe when the relatively unaversive airpuff serves as the US.

It has been reported that, although original differential conditioning is not impaired, reversal conditioning is severely impaired by mPFC lesions (Chachich and Powell, 1999), again an effect similar to hippocampal lesions (Buchanan and Powell, 1980). In a recent experiment the effects of continuous (100%) versus partial (25%) reinforcement on Pavlovian delay and trace EB conditioning was studied in rabbits with either mPFC lesions or sham lesions (Powell, Churchwell and Burriss, 2005). mPFC lesions impaired trace conditioning in both reinforcement conditions. Partial reinforcement retarded EB conditioning in both the trace and delay paradigms, but this impairment was significantly greater during trace conditioning in rabbits with mPFC lesions. These experiments thus clearly demonstrate that damage to the mPFC produces differential impairments in EB conditioning when non-optimal conditioning parameters are employed. These conditions include reversal training, trace conditioning, and partial reinforcement.

4.3. Studies of Post-Training mPFC Lesions on Trace Eyeblink Conditioning

Post-training lesions of the mPFC also produce a dramatic effect on the subsequent performance of the EB response (Powell, Skaggs, Churchwell and McLaughlin, 2001), suggesting that the effects of mPFC damage on EB conditioning involve memory rather than encoding processes. Although a small effect is obtained during delay conditioning, a more severe deficit is produced when the trace conditioning paradigm is employed. Accompanying HR changes, however, are unaffected. This aspect of mPFC control of EB conditioning has been studied in some detail in both rabbits and rats. In a recent experiment (Simon, Knuckley, Churchwell and Powell, 2005) rabbits were trained on trace eyeblink conditioning until they reached a criterion of ten consecutive EB conditioned responses. Electrolytic lesions were then made in the mPFC centered on Brodmann's area 32 at five different time intervals after training. These included immediately, 24 hours, 1 week, 2 weeks, and 1 month after training. Separate groups of animals received sham lesions at the same time intervals after training. After a two week post-operative recovery period, all animals were retested for three days on trace conditioning using the same parameters that were employed during pre-operative training. Substantial EB performance deficits occurred in the animals with mPFC lesions, compared to sham lesioned animals, on the first day of retesting in all five groups. However, by the second or third day of retesting the rabbits with lesions were performing at a level that was comparable to that of sham animals. Animals that received more posterolateral lesions of neocortex, however, did not show post-operative conditioning deficits, suggesting that damage to area 32 is required to produce these deficits. Moreover, a comparison of percentage EB CRs of animals with post-operative damage with that of animals that received mPFC lesions before training, suggests that mPFC post-training lesions produced damage to a retrieval process and not to storage or an acquisition process.

A recently completed study (Oswald, Maddox and Powell, 2006) further supports these conclusions. In this experiment rabbits were trained on trace eyeblink conditioning to criterion of 10 consecutive EB CRs. One week following acquisition, ibotenic acid lesions or sham surgeries were made in the mPFC centered on area 32. Following a one week post-operative recovery period all animals were retrained for 4 consecutive days using the same parameters, given one week off and then retrained for another 4 days. Mean EB conditioning performance deficits in the lesioned group occurred on the first and second days of both 1-week and 2-week post-training periods. However, by the third and fourth day of retraining, like the animals in the earlier study, lesioned animals were performing at a level comparable to that of the sham animals. These findings strongly indicate that the mPFC is involved in retrieval rather than consolidation or storage since lesioned animals were impaired at both retesting times, but were able to relearn the task. Also the fact that ibotenic acid was employed, which destroys only the soma, and not fibers of passage, suggests that intrinsic mPFC cells are involved in this retrieval process.

Similar studies have been reported by Takehara and colleagues in rodents (Takehara, Kawahara, Takatsuki and Kirino, 2002; Takehara, Kawahara and Kiriono, 2003; Takahara-Nishiuchi, Kawahara and Kirino, 2005). In a first experiment, rats received aspiration lesions of the hippocampus, prefrontal cortex, or cerebellum after they had learned a trace EB conditioning task to a criterion. As expected, hippocampal lesions impaired performance only early during post-operative testing. However, lesions of the mPFC produced post-operative performance deficits at one and two weeks or one month following training. Unlike the study in rabbits reported above, however, mPFC lesions in rats appeared to produce increasingly greater performance deficits as a function of length of time after training that the lesion was made. It is difficult to understand why lesions that interfered with more remote memory had the greatest effect in this study, whereas in the study by Simon et al (2005) this was not the case. However, like the rabbit study, the study by Takehara et al (2003) in rats showed that mPFC lesions produced their greatest performance deficits on first post-operative testing day, but performance approached that of sham animals by day 3.

Takehara et al (2003), as well as Christian and Thompson (2003) suggest that mPFC processing of information results in a reorganization of memory processes from temporary storage in the hippocampus to more permanent storage in the mPFC. However, the results of the papers by Simon et al (2005) and Oswald et al (2006) suggest that mPFC is important in retrieval and not storage of information. A subsequent study by Takehara-Nishiuchi, Nakao, Kawahara, Matsuki and Kirino (2006) was designed to further investigate this possibility. In this experiment, NMDA receptor blockade in the mPFC was applied during the first or two weeks after initial training, which resulted in marked impairments in memory retention measured 6 weeks after training. However, the same treatment had no effect if performed during the third or fourth weeks following training. The authors suggest that their results indicate that successful establishment of remotely acquired memory requires activation of NMDA receptors in the mPFC at least during the initial week of the post-learning period. The present author suggests, based on a wide range of available data as described above, that permanent storage of the EB CR in both trace and delay conditioning is in the deep nuclei of the cerebellum.

4.4. Studies of Appetitive Conditioning

Recent experiments have shown that damage to the mPFC also impairs JM conditioning (McLaughlin and Powell, 1999), but the HR changes in this case are unaffected. Similar experiments, in which post-training lesions were studied on JM conditioning, also revealed lesion-induced deficits in JM performance, compared to rabbits with sham lesions (McLaughlin, Powell and White, 2002), and, like the EB experiments, the accompanying CS-evoked HR changes were unaffected by the lesion. These findings are extremely important since they suggest that the mPFC is involved in retrieval of memories necessary for evoking learned somatomotor behaviors, as noted previously (McLaughlin and Powell, 1999; Powell et al, 2002).

Electrophysiological recording studies have also focused on mPFC participation in JM conditioning. In a recent experiment, single unit discharge was assessed in a differential aversive/appetitive conditioning paradigm, in which one CS signaled water, another eyeshock, and a third no US (McLaughlin, Powell and White, 2002). The signal associated with water produced pronounced reliable JM conditioning, while the signal associated with eyeshock produced EB conditioning; somatomotor responses to the third signal were nonassociative. Accompanying CS-evoked single unit activity in area 32 showed a variety of CS-related changes; interestingly some cells responded to the appetitive signal, while a different population of cells responded to the aversive signal. However, several cells responded to both CSs. This experiment thus suggests a heterogeneous population of units in the mPFC that respond to classical conditioning contingencies of both a defensive as well as appetitive nature.

Another interesting model of appetitive conditioning in rodents has been described by Holland (1977, 1984). This investigator determined that there were two types of classically conditioned behavior in rats in appetitive food situations. First, a conditioning-dependent enhancement of orienting responses elicited by the CS prior to conditioning occurs, and second, behaviors which were originally evoked by the food US, but not the CS, also occur. With regard to the latter, both visual and auditory CSs come to elicit behaviors that resemble those elicited by food delivery itself; "rats stand relatively motionless with their heads inserted in the recessed area where food is delivered and/or make short, rapid movements of the head toward the food cup". These behaviors are described by Holland as "US generated" behaviors. However, in addition to these US-elicited behaviors, both auditory and visual CSs also acquire CS-related cues that are specifically oriented toward the CS. Food reinforced visual cues come to elicit rearing of the hind legs and orientation towards a light source, whereas auditory cues produce a conditioned startle response.

Gallagher, Graham and Holland (1990) determined that lesions of the central nucleus of the amygdala abolished CS-generated CRs to both visual and auditory CSs, although the original orienting responses and habituation to CSs were comparable in the lesion and control groups. However, rats with central nucleus lesions readily acquired the US generated CRs. These conditioned behaviors have not been studied as a function of medial prefrontal damage, but Gallagher, McMahan and Schoenbaum (1999) found that orbitofrontal cortex lesions did not abolish the initial acquisition of CS-related behaviors, nor did the lesions abolish taste aversion learning during a second training phase. However, in a test for devaluation of the reinforcer lesioned rats exhibited no change in conditioned responding to the CS, which contrasted with control rats in which devaluation of the US produced a significant decrease in approach to the food cup during presentation of the CS. Although preliminary, the results using this rodent model of appetitive classical conditioning is compatible with the work that has been done previously in the rabbit, as described above.

5. ROLE OF mPFC IN EXTINCTION

Also as described above, there has been increased recent interest in the neural mechanisms of extinction of both autonomic and somatomotor conditioned responses. Extinction is defined as a decrease in CR frequency and/or amplitude that results from the removal of the unconditioned stimulus from the contingency; i.e., the CS is presented alone unpaired with the US. Although Pavlov (1927) discovered and used the term extinction in his now famous classical conditioning experiments in dogs, recent research has revealed that extinction procedures are much more complex than early investigators originally thought. It is now accepted that extinction is not simply a decline in responses due to a temporal or "forgetting" process, but is most likely due to acquisition of an active inhibitory process that is itself associative in nature. This idea is very similar to Pavlov's original concept of conditioned inhibition (Pavlov, 1927). Robleto, Poulos and Thompson (2004) recently reviewed possible brain mechanisms involved in extinction of the classically conditioned EB response, and Myers and Davis (2002) have published a similar review of the behavioral and neural analysis of extinction of fear conditioning. It is important to note that the recent interest in extinction has an applied basis, since the experimental analysis of fear conditioning has been viewed as an animal model of the anxiety neuroses (Myers and Davis, 2002). Thus, the neural mechanisms by which fear is inhibited is important information for clinical intervention of patients suffering from fear disregulation.

Myers and Davis (2002) concluded that, on the whole, the search for an inhibitory brain structure has not been very fruitful, as no one structure has emerged that appears to be essential for extinction. A good deal of early work focused on the hippocampus and its septal connections as a possible mechanism underlying extinction (Schmajuk, 1984; Thomas and Gash, 1988). Other studies suggest that the amygdala mediates extinction, as well as acquisition of fear conditioning, as recently reviewed by Kim and Jung (2006). More recent work has focused upon the sensory cortex (Quirk, Armony and LeDoux, 1997). However, again data on the role of the sensory cortex in extinction have not been convincing. More recent research, which shows some promise, however, are studies involving the prefrontal cortex. Quirk et al (1997) and LeDoux et al (1989) in their studies of the sensory cortical control of extinction both felt that the sensory cortex likely feeds extinction-related information forward to other cortical areas, such as the PFC. Morgan, Romanski and LeDoux (1993) reported that mPFC lesions had no effect on initial acquisition of fear conditioning, but retarded subsequent extinction to a tone CS. However, as described above, similar work conducted by Gerwitz et al (1997) and Quirk et al (2000) found no differences between lesion and control groups on extinction. More recently, however, Quirk et al (2000) performed an experiment that appears to resolve these inconsistencies. These investigators examined the effects of PFC lesions on acquisition, extinction and recovery of conditioned fear responses over two days. On the first day PFC lesions had no effect on acquisition or extinction of conditioned freezing or suppression of bar pressing. However, on the following day sham rats had recovered only 27% of their acquired freezing, whereas lesioned rats recovered 86%, which was not significantly different from a control group that never received extinction. These data thus suggest that the PFC is involved in consolidation of extinction learning. Even more importantly, Milad and Quirk (2002) found that neurons in the ventral mPFC (i.e., the infralimbic cortex; Brodmann's area 25) showed increased activity, not during acquisition of a bar suppression and freezing response, but during its extinction, thus implicating area 25 in extinction of fear conditioning.

With regard to extinction of the EB CR, Krupa and Thompson (2003) showed that blocking expression of the CR can block extinction. These investigators inactivated the motor nuclei necessary for expression of the EB CR during CS alone extinction training, which resulted in complete prevention of extinction over three to six days. The interpostius nucleus of the cerebellum is also widely regarded to be necessary for acquisition and expression of the EB CR (see above). Hardiman, Ramnani and Yeo (1996) have reported that reversible inactivation of the interpositus nuclear region with muscimol during CS alone extinction training also completely prevented extinction and expression of the CR. These results were replicated by Robelto and Thompson (2003). These data thus seem to implicate the interpositus nucleus in extinction, as well as acquisition of the EB CR, similar to the role that the amygdala plays with regard to fear conditioning, as described above. Another brain stem structure possibly involved in EB extinction is the inferior olive (IO) (Medina et al, 2002; Nelson et al, 1989; Thompson, 2005). Like the study of fear extinction, the hippocampus was shown in earlier studies to be involved in somatomotor extinction, but the hippocampus does not appear to be essential for extinction of the delay CR (e.g., Moyer et al, 1990). There have been no studies of the role of the prefrontal cortex in extinction of somatomotor learning.

6. PAVLOVIAN CONDITIONING AND mPFC FUNCTION

Neuronal activity in the PFC is necessary for maintaining information related to ongoing sensory stimulation. O'Reilly (2006) in a recent review points out that mPFC shows sustained neural firing that is robust in the face of potentially distracting information, which allows a focus on the task at hand to the exclusion of all other distracting information, suggesting that the mPFC may be characterized as inhibiting task-irrelevant information. However, an equally important characteristic of mPFC function is that this maintenance of context must be rapidly updated by ongoing changes in stimulation. Such changes are critical for behavioral flexibility, viz. the ability to quickly adapt to the changing demands of the environment. The rapid updating of information in the mPFC is presumed to occur as a result of dynamic gating mechanisms which modulate the stability of mPFC active maintenance (O'Reilly, 2006). O'Reilly suggests that two basic mechanisms exist for carrying out this activity, which involve opening a gate to ongoing mPFC function as a result of a) actions of the neuromodulator dopamine and b) actions of the neostriatum and thalamus, which provide either a "go" or "no go" status to the mPFC.

A major question then is how the effects of mPFC manipulations on Pavlovian conditioning can be integrated with these models. Clearly, occurrence of a CS provides information that requires updating the sensory status of the mPFC. The present findings suggest that this is a multi-stage process, and as noted above, a multi-stage model of Pavlovian conditioning is illustrated in Figure 5. At it simplest and most empirical level, however, three hierarchically arranged and sequentially identifiable stages of information processing are involved in any task that involves associative learning. These include (a) non-specific trace registration associated with attentional processes, such as those underlying orienting and non-associative forms of learning (Stage 1 in Figure 5); (b) the initial registration of associative stimulus significance, as reflected, for example, by the development of non-specific (i.e., visceral) CRs (Stage 2 in Figure 5); and (c) the elaboration of situationally appropriate (i.e., adaptive) somatomotor CRs (stages 3 and 4 of Figure 5. The latter would include for example EB or NM CRs. According to this model changes in the limbic forebrain, including the mPFC, are an integral basis of stage 2 memory traces (e.g., see Buchanan and Powell, 1982a), whereas extrapyramidal (especially cerebellar) plasticity mediates stage 4 memories. Other evidence, as described in Powell and Levine-Bryce (1989), suggest that hypothalamic mechanisms may be sufficient for producing the autonomic changes associated with stage 1 ORs and their habituation.

Information processing theory may provide an heuristic model for understanding mPFC's participation in this process. According to information processing models external stimuli are first processed in a sensory register and those stimuli that are significant are further processed by an attention mechanism and stored in short term or working memory. Working memory has access to least two long term memory registers: i.e., declarative and procedural registers. Declarative memory refers to memory for facts of semantic or episodic nature, and is discussed at some length above. It is thus memory that is available to consciousness, and which therefore can be declared. Procedural memory on the other hand is rule-based memory and contains the habits and skills necessary for dealing with objects both physical and symbolic in one's environment.

Based on such a model, it is suggested that stimuli are selected from the typically defined sensory registers to be placed in working or short term memory if they are (a) novel, or (b) serve as signals for reinforcers (i.e., USs). For this process to function adequately with regard to the second of these principles (i.e., reinforcement) it must sample or in some way come into contact with the current motivational state of the organism. Consequently, there must be another kind of register (or cognitive process) that is sensitive to the current motivational state of the organism and which compares the events in sensory memory with previously occurring events presumably in working memory, to determine if any are signals for reinforcers that are germane to this motivational state. For this reason the present author has suggested that a "reinforcement cue register" is a necessary part of mPFC function (Powell et al, 1990; see Figure 12). The events contained in such a register must come to be there as a consequence of learning. Such learning would consist of classical conditioning, since the events to be compared are signals. Hence, the rehearsal process is an important mechanism for determining not only the contents of long term memory, but also the contents of the reinforcement cue register. In fact the contents of this register might be expected to come directly from working memory based upon the number of previous pairings of the events, i.e., the CS and reinforcer, as well as the current motivational status of the organism. The operation of this register is thus based on an mPFC comparison of events in the sensory register with those in the reinforcement cue register. If a match occurs this event determines the procedure that ultimately produces the desired behavior (also see Gray, 1982).

At a neurophysiological level the occurrence of a specific need must allow the reinforcement cue register selection process access to those neuronal cells or cell systems that have previously signaled the occurrence of reinforcers that met these particular needs. In essence then, the reinforcement cue register may be conceived as providing momentary access to the comparator and working memory in the mPFC to determine whether the current contents of the sensory register match any stimuli that have been highlighted in short term memory by current motivational status as being important. The reinforcement cue register thus would not consist of reinforcing stimuli per se, but rather signals (viz. cues) that previously predicted reinforcers associated with the current motivational status. It would therefore consist of the representations of conditional reinforcers. More importantly, for present purposes it is further suggested that the mPFC plays a major role in the establishment of the secondary reinforcing properties of the cues associated with reinforcers by providing these signals with affective qualities.

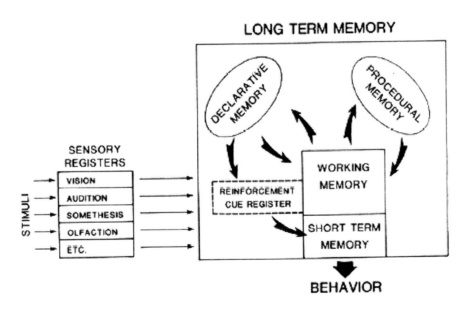

Figure 12. Diagram of brain processing model illustrating the relationship between a postulated "reinforcement cue register" which compares incoming information from sensory systems with elements of working memory, which have been highlighted by current motivational status. A possible role for the mPFC is to associate the signals in such a register with their affective significance. (From Powell, 1989).

It is clear that the affective characteristics of stimuli are not represented physically, (i.e., neurally) in the mPFC, but rather that the mPFC is involved in establishing the importance of such stimuli via a comparison process such as that described above. This is the familiar question of whether acquisition, encoding, storage of information, or retrieval of memory is involved. Considerable evidence suggests that, although such a process might involve mPFC function, no permanent neural representations are stored in the mPFC. Rather the mPFC is involved only in increasing the momentary activation of a subset of neural elements that are simultaneously represented in the sensory registers and in the reinforcement cue register of working memory. The findings of Orona and Gabriel (1983), for example, that MUA in the mPFC reaches a maximum during differential avoidance conditioning long before the behavioral discrimination is made supports this hypothesis. Similarly, CS-evoked multiple unit activity of the mPFC increases initially during acquisition of the cardiac changes associated with Pavlovian conditioning but declines during later trials (Gibbs and Powell, 1988). Also supporting this hypothesis is data described above, which indicates that the essential aspect of this mechanism is associated with retrieval of the CS/US engram from permanent storage in the cerebellum (Simon et al, 2005). Such retrieval would obviously only occur when there is a match of stimuli in the reinforcement cue register with relevant cues in the sensory register.

7. SUMMARY

The prefrontal cortex is a complex heterogeneous structure, which provides for analysis and processing of information related to decision making, based on a variety of information, including the affective properties of stimuli. The present review has focused on this latter aspect of prefrontal functioning and has been limited to the medial prefrontal cortex, since it has been demonstrated that this area of the PFC participates in Pavlovian conditioning of visceral responses. A major point has been made that Pavlovian conditioning consists of a multi-process or set of procedures involving on the one hand non-specific, primarily visceral or autonomic responses, and on the other associative learning underlying conditioning of specific somatomotor responses. An attempt has been made to place the experimental paradigms of various classical conditioning procedures in the context of overall mPFC function. While the emphasis has been on Pavlovian conditioning procedures, it is clear that this is only one aspect of mPFC processing. It is, nevertheless, an important aspect of mPFC functioning, since associative learning is one of the major ways in which new information is acquired and processed so as to produce adaptive somatomotor behaviors. Although much is known about this aspect of mPFC function, obviously considerable questions remain to be answered. One of the purposes of the present review is not only to provide information regarding mPFC control of Pavlovian conditioning, but to raise questions which still need to be answered by future research.

ACKNOWLEDGEMENTS

Preparation of this paper was supported by DVA Institutional Medical Research funds awarded to the William Jennings Bryan Dorn VA Medical Center. The author thanks Elizabeth Hamel for assistance with manuscript preparation and Andrew Pringle, Jr. for preparation of the illustrations. I am also grateful to Geoff Collier, Barbara Oswald, Jim Appel, and Jack Ginsberg, all of whom read and made insightful comments on an earlier version of this manuscript.

REFERENCES

Adolphs, R. (1999). The human amygdala and emotion. *Neuroscientist*, 5, 125-137.

Albiniak, B. A., and Powell, D. A. (1980). Peripheral autonomic mechanisms and Pavlovian conditioning in the rabbit (oryctolagus cuniculus). *Journal of Comparative and Physiological Psychology*, 94, 1101-1113.

Bard, P., and Mountcastle, V. B. (1948). Some forebrain mechanisms involved in expression of rage with special reference to suppression of angry behavior. *Research Publications of the Association of Nervous and Mental Diseases*, 27, 362-404.

Blanchard, R. J., Blanchard, D. C., Agullana, R., and Weiss, S. M. (1991). Twenty-two khz alarm cries to presentation of a predator, by laboratory rats living in visible burrow systems. *Physiology and Behavior*, 50, 967-972.

Buchanan, S. L. (1991). Differential and reversal Pavlovian conditioning in rabbits with mediodorsal thalamic lesions: Assessment of heart rate and eyeblink responses. *Experimental Brain Research*, 86, 174-181.

Buchanan, S. L., and Powell, D. A. (1980). Divergencies in Pavlovian conditioned heart rate and eyeblink responses produced by hippocampectomy in the rabbit. *Behavioral and Neural Biology*, 30, 20-38.

Buchanan, S. L., and Powell, D. A. (1982a). Cingulate cortex: Its role in Pavlovian conditioning. *Journal of Comparative and Physiological Psychology*, 96, 755-774.

Buchanan, S. L., and Powell, D. A. (1982b). Cingulate damage attentuates conditioned bradycardia. *Neuroscience Letters*, 29, 261-268.

Buchanan, S. L., and Powell, D. A. (1989). Parasagittal thalamic knife cuts and cardiac changes. *Behavioural Brain Research*, 32, 241-253.

Buchanan, S. L., and Thompson, R. H. (1990). Mediodorsal thalamic lesions and Pavlovian conditioning of heart rate and eyeblink responses in the rabbit. *Behavioral Neuroscience*, 104, 912-918.

Buchanan, S. L., Penney, J., Tebbutt, D., and Powell, D. A. (1997). Lesions of the mediodorsal nucleus of the thalamus and classical eyeblink conditioning under less than optimal stimulus conditions: Role of partial reinforcement and interstimulus interval. *Behavioral Neuroscience*, 111, 1075-1085.

Buchanan, S. L., Thompson, R. H., Maxwell, B. L., and Powell, D. A. (1994). Efferent connections of the medial prefrontal cortex in the rabbit. *Experimental Brain Research*, 100, 469-483.

Buchanan, S. L., Valentine, J. D., and Powell, D. A. (1985). Autonomic responses are elicited by electrical stimulation of the medial but not lateral frontal cortex in rabbits. *Behavioural Brain Research*, 18, 51-62.

Buckner, R. L., and Petersen, S. E. (1996). What does neuroimaging tell us about the role of prefrontal cortex in memory retrieval? *Seminars in the Neurosciences*, 8, 47-55.

Chachich, M. E., and Powell, D. A. (2004). The role of claustrum in Pavlovian heart rate conditioning in the rabbit (oryctolagus cuniculus): Anatomical, electrophysiological, and lesion studies. *Behavioral Neuroscience*, 118, 514-525.

Chachich, M., and Powell, D. A. (1999). Both medial prefrontal and amygdala central nucleus lesions abolish heart rate classical conditioning, but only prefrontal lesions impair reversal of eyeblink differential conditioning. *Neuroscience Letters*, 257, 151-154.

Chachich, M., Buchanan, S., and Powell, D. A. (1997). *Characterization of single-unit activity in the mediodorsal nucleus of the thalamus during expression of differential heart rate conditioning in the rabbit.* 129-141.

Chachich, M., Penney, J., and Powell, D. A. (1996). Subicular lesions disrupt but do not abolish classically conditioned bradycardia in rabbits. *Behavioral Neuroscience*, 110, 707-717.

Christian, K. M., and Thompson, R. F. (2003). Neural substrates of eyeblink conditioning: Acquisition and retention. *Learning and Memory*, 11, 427-455.

Clark, R. E., and Squire, L. R. (1998). Classical conditioning and brain systems: The role of awareness. *Science*, 280, 77-81.

Clark, R. E., Manns, J. R., and Squire, L. R. (2001). Trace and delay eyeblink conditioning: Contrasting phenomena of declarative and nondeclarative memory. *Psychological Science*, 12, 304-308.

Cohen, D. H., and Randall, D. C. (1984). Classical conditioning of cardiovascular responses. *Annual Review of Physiology*, 46, 187-197.

Damasio, A. R. (1994). *Descartes error - emotion, reason and the human brain*. New York, NY: GP Putnam.

Daum, I., Channon, S., and Gray, J. A. (1992). Classical conditioning after temporal lobe lesions in man: Sparing of simple discrimination and extinction. *Behavioural Brain Research*, 52, 159-165.

Daum, I., Channon, S., Polkey, C. E., and Gray, J. A. (1991). Classical conditioning after temporal lobe lesions in man: Impairment in conditional discrimination. *Behavioral Neuroscience*, 105, 396-408.

Daum, I., Schugens, M. M., Ackermann, H., Lutzenberger, W., Dichgans, J., and Birbaumer, N. (1993). Classical conditioning after cerebellar lesions in humans. *Behavioral Neuroscience*, 107, 748-756.

Daum, I., Schugens, M. M., Breitenstein, C., Topka, H., and Spieker, S. (1996). Classical eyeblink conditioning in parkinson's disease. *Movement Disorders*, 11, 639-646.

Davis, M. (1997). Neurobiology of fear responses: The role of the amygdala. *Journal of Neuropsychiatry and Clinical Neurosciences*, 9, 382-402.

Dykman, R. A., Mack, R. L., and Ackerman, P. T. (1965). The evolution of autonomic and motor components of the non-avoidance conditioned response in the dog. *Psychophysiology*, 1, 209-230.

Fanselow, M. S. (1986). Conditioned fear-induced opiate analgesia: A competing motivational state theory of stress analgesia. *Annals of the New York Academy of Sciences*, 476, 40-54.

Fuster, J. M. (1997). *The prefrontal cortex: Anatomy, physiology, and neuropsychology of the frontal lobe*. Philadelphia, PA: Lippincott-Raven.

Gabrieli, J. D. E., McGlinchey-Berroth, R., Carrillo, M. C., Gluck, M. A., Cermak, L. S., and Disterhoft, J. F. (1995). Intact delay-eyeblink classical conditioning in amnesia. *Behavioral Neuroscience*, 109, 819-827.

Gallagher, M., Graham, P. W., and Holland, P. C. (1990). The amygdala central nucleus and appetitive Pavlovian conditioning: Lesions impair one class of conditioned behavior. *The Journal of Neuroscience*, 10, 1906-1911.

Gallagher, M., McMahan, R. W., and Schoenbaum, G. (1999). Orbitofrontal cortex and representation of incentive value in associative learning. *The Journal of Neuroscience*, 19, 6610-6614.

Gewirtz, J. C., Falls, W. A., and Davis, M. (1997). Normal conditioned inhibition and extinction of freezing and fear-potentiated startle following electrolytic lesions of medial prefrontal cortex in rats. *Behavioral Neuroscience*, 111, 712-726.

Gibbs, C. M., and Powell, D. A. (1988). Neuronal correlates of classically conditioned bradycardia in the rabbit: Studies of the medial prefrontal cortex. *Brain Research*, 442, 86-96.

Gibbs, C. M., and Powell, D. A. (1991). Single-unit activity in the dorsomedial prefrontal cortex during the expression of discriminative bradycardia in rabbits. *Behavioural Brain Research*, 43, 79-92.

Gibbs, C. M., Prescott, L. B., and Powell, D. A. (1992). A comparison of multiple-unit activity in the medial prefrontal and agranular insular cortices during Pavlovian heart rate conditioning in rabbits. *Experimental Brain Research*, 89, 599-610.

Goldman-Rakic, P. S., and Selemon, L. D. (1997). Functional and anatomical aspects of prefrontal pathology in schizophrenia. *Schizophrenia Bulletin*, 23, 437-458.

Gormezano, I. (1966). Classical conditioning. In J. B. Sidowski (Ed.), *Experimental methods and instrumentation in psychology* (pp. 385-420). New York NY: McGraw Hill.

Gormezano, I. (1972). *Investigations of defense and reward conditioning in the rabbit.* In A. H. Black and W. F. Prokasy (Eds.), . York, NY: Appleton-Century-Crofts.

Gormezano, I., and Coleman, S. R. (1973). The law of effect and CR contingent modification of the ucs. *Conditional Reflex*, 8, 41-56.

Gray, J. A. (1982). *The neuropsychology of anxiety: An inquiry into the functions of the septo-hippocampal system.* New York NY: Oxford University Press.

Groenewegen, H. J., Berendse, H. W., and Haber, S. N. (1993). Organization of the output of the ventral striatopallidal system in the rat: Ventral pallidal efferents. *Neuroscience*, 57, 113-142.

Hardiman, M. J., Ramnani, N., and Yeo, C. H. (1996). Reversible inactivations of the cerebellum with muscimol prevent the acquisition and extinction of conditioned nictitating membrane responses in the rabbit. *Experimental Brain Research*, 110, 235-247.

Holland, P. C. (1977). Conditioned stimulus as a determinant of the form of the Pavlovian conditioned response. *Journal of Experimental Psychology*, 3, 77-104.

Holland, P. C. (1984). Origins of behavior in Pavlovian conditioning. *Psychology, Learning and Motivation*, 18, 129-174.

Houk, J. C., and Wise, S. P. (1995). Distributed modular architectures linking basal ganglia, cerebellum, and cerebral cortex: Their role in planning and controlling action. *Cerebral Cortex*, 5, 95-110.

Ison, J. R., and Hoffman, H. S. (1983). Reflex modification in the domain of startle: Ii. The anomalous history of a robust and ubiquitous phenomenon. *Psychological Bulletin*, 94, 3-17.

James, G. O., Hardiman, M. J., and Yeo, C. H. (1987). Hippocampal lesions and trace conditioning in the rabbit. *Behavioural Brain Research*, 23, 109-116.

Joseph, J. A., and Powell, D. A. (1980). Peripheral 6-hydroxydopamine administration in the rabbit (oryctolagus cuniculus): Effects on Pavlovian conditioning. *Journal of Comparative and Physiological Psychology*, 94, 1114-1125.

Kaada, B. R. (1951). Somato-motor, autonomic and electrocorticographic responses to electrical stimulation of rhinencephalic and other structures in primates, cat and dog. *Acta Physiologica Scandinavica*, 23, 1-285.

Kao, K. T., and Powell, D. A. (1988). Lesions of the substantia nigra retard Pavlovian eyeblink but not heart rate conditioning in the rabbit. *Behavioral Neuroscience*, 102, 515-525.

Kapp, B. S., Frysinger, R. C., Gallagher, M., and Haselton, J. R. (1979). Amygdala central nucleus lesions: Effect on heart rate conditioning in the rabbit. *Physiology and Behavior*, 23, 1109-1117.

Kapp, B. S., Gallagher, M., Underwood, M. D., McNall, C. L., and Whitehorn, D. (1982). Cardiovascular responses elicited by electrical stimulation of the amygdala central nucleus in the rabbit. *Brain Research*, 234, 251-262.

Kazis, E., Duncan, S., and Powell, D. A. (1973). *Cholinergic and adrenergic control of heart rate changes in the rabbit*. Bulletin of the Psychonomic Society, 3, 41-43.

Kazis, E., Milligan, W. L., and Powell, D. A. (1973). Autonomic-somatic relationships: Blockade of heart rate and corneoretinal potential. *Journal of Comparative Physiological Psychology*, 84, 98-110.

Kehoe, E. J., and Macrae, M. (1994). Classical conditioning of the rabbit nictitating membrane response can be fast or slow: Implications for lennartz and weinberger's (1992) two-factor theory. *Psychobiology*, 22, 1-4.

Kihlstrom, J. F. (1987). The cognitive unconscious. Science, 237, 1445-1452.

Kim, J. J., and Jung, M. W. (2006). Neural circuits and mechanisms involved in Pavlovian fear conditioning: A critical review. *Neuroscience and Biobehavioral Reviews*, 30, 188-202.

Kronforst-Collins, M. A., and Disterhoft, J. F. (1998). Lesions of the caudal area of rabbit medial prefrontal cortex impair trace eyeblink conditioning. *Neurobiology of Learning and Memory*, 69, 147-162.

Krupa, D. J., and Thompson, R. F. (2003). Inhibiting the expression of a classically conditioned behavior prevents its extinction. *Journal of Neuroscience*, 23, 10577-10584.

Lavond, D. G., Lincoln, J. S., McCormick, D. A., and Thompson, R. F. (1984). Effect of bilateral lesions of the dentate and interpositus cerebellar nuclei on conditioning of heart-rate and nictitating membrane/eyelid responses in the rabbit. *Brain Research*, 305, 323-330.

LeDoux, J. E. (2000). Emotion circuits in the brain. *Annual Review of Neuroscience*, 23, 155-184.

LeDoux, J. E., Romanski, L., and Xagoraris, A. (1989). Indelibility of subcortical emotional memories. *Journal of Cognitive Neuroscience*, 1, 238-243.

LeDoux, J. E., Sakaguchi, A., Iwata, J., and Reis, D. J. (1986). Interruption of projections from the medial geniculate body to an arch-neostriatal field disrupts the classical conditioning of emotional responses to acoustic stimuli. *Neuroscience*, 17, 615-627.

Lee, T., and Kim, J. J. (2004). Differential effects of cerebellar, amygdalar, and hippocampal lesions on classical eyeblink conditioning in rats. *The Journal of Neuroscience*, 24, 3242-3250.

Lennartz, R. C., and Weinberger, N. M. (1992). Analysis of response systems in Pavlovian conditioning reveals rapidly versus slowly acquired conditioned responses: Support for two factors, implications for behavior and neurobiology. *Psychobiology*, 20, 93-119.

Lennartz, R. C., and Weinberger, N. M. (1994). A comparison of nonspecific and nictitating membrane conditioned responses: Additional support for two-factor theories. *Psychobiology*, 22, 5-15.

Lofving, B. (1961). Cardiovascular adjustments induced from the rostral cingulate gyrus, with special reference to sympatho-inhibitory mechanisms. *Acta Physiologica Scandinavica*, 53 (Suppl. 184), 1-82.

Manns, J. R., Clark, R. E., and Squire, L. R. (2000). Awareness predicts the magnitude of single-cue trace eyeblink conditioning. *Hippocampus*, 10, 181-186.

Maxwell, B., Powell, D. A., and Buchanan, S. L. (1994). Multiple and single unit activity in area 32 (prelimbic region) of the medial prefrontal cortex during Pavlovian heart rate conditioning in the rabbit. *Cerebral Cortex*, 4, 230-246.

McDonald, A. J. (1991). Organization of amygdaloid projections to the prefrontal cortex and associated striatum in the rat. *Neuroscience*, 44, 1-14.

McGlinchey-Berroth, R., Carrillo, M. C., Gabrieli, J. D. E., Brawn, C. M., and Disterhoft, J. F. (1997). Impaired trace eyeblink conditioning in bilateral, medial-temporal lobe amnesia. *Behavioral Neuroscience*, 111, 873-882.

McLaughlin, J., and Powell, D. A. (1999). Pavlovian heart rate and jaw movement conditioning in the rabbit: Effects of medial prefrontal lesions. *Neurobiology of Learning and Memory*, 71, 150-166.

McLaughlin, J., Flaten, M. A., Chachich, M., and Powell, D. A. (2001). Medial prefrontal lesions attenuate conditioned reflex facilitation but do not affect prepulse modification of the eyeblink reflex in rabbits. *Experimental Brain Research*, 140, 318-325.

McLaughlin, J., Powell, D. A., and White, J. D. (2002). Characterization of the neuronal changes in the medial prefrontal cortex during jaw movement and eyeblink Pavlovian conditioning in the rabbit. *Behavioural Brain Research*, 132, 117-133.

McLaughlin, J., Skaggs, H., Churchwell, J., and Powell, D. A. (2002). Medial prefrontal cortex and Pavlovian conditioning: Trace versus delay conditioning. *Behavioral Neuroscience*, 116, 37-47.

Medina, J. F., Repa, J. C., Mauk, M. D., and LeDoux, J. E. (2002). Parallels between cerebellum- and amygdala-dependent conditioning. *Nature Reviews Neuroscience*, 3, 122-131.

Middleton, F. A., and Strick, P. L. (1994). Anatomical evidence for cerebellar and basal ganglia involvement in higher cognitive function. *Science*, 266, 458-461.

Milad, M. R., and Quirk, G. J. (2002). Neurons in medial prefrontal cortex signal memory for fear extinction. *Nature*, 420, 70-74.

Mogensen, G. J., Ciriello, J., Garland, J., and Wu, M. (1987). Ventral pallidum projections to mediodorsal nucleus of the thalamus: An anatomical and electrophysiological investigation in the rat. *Brain Research*, 404, 221-230.

Morgan, M. A., and LeDoux, J. E. (1995). Differential contribution of dorsal and ventral medial prefrontal cortex to acquisition and extinction of conditioned fear in rats. *Behavioral Neuroscience*, 109, 681-688.

Morgan, M. A., Romanski, L. M., and LeDoux, J. E. (1993). Extinction of emotional learning: Contribution of medial prefrontal cortex. *Neuroscience Letters*, 163, 109-113.

Moyer, J. R., Jr., Deyo, R. A., and Disterhoft, J. F. (1990). Hippocampectomy disrupts trace eye-blink conditioning in rabbits. *Behavioral Neuroscience*, 104, 243-252.

Myers, K. M., and Davis, M. (2002). Behavioral and neural analysis of extinction. *Neuron*, 36, 567-584.

Nelson, B. J., Adams, J. C., Barmack, N. H., and Mugnaini, E. (1989). Comparative study of glutamate decarboxylase immunoreactive boutons in the mammalian inferior olive. *Journal of Comparative Neurology*, 286, 514-539.

Obrist, P. A. (1981). *Cardiovascular psychophysiology: A perspective*. New York, New York: Plenum Press.

Ohman, A. (1988). Nonconscious control of autonomic responses: A role for Pavlovian conditioning? *Biological Psychology*, 27, 113-135.

Olton, D. S. (1979). Mazes, maps, and memory. *American Psychologist*, 34, 583-596.

O'Reilly, R. C. (2006). Biologically based computational models of high-level cognition. *Science*, 314, 91-94.

Orona, E., and Gabriel, M. (1983). Multiple-unit activity of the prefrontal cortex and mediodorsal thalamic nucleus during acquisition of discriminative avoidance behavior in rabbits. *Brain Research*, 263, 295-312.

Oswald, B., Knuckley, B., Mahan, K., Sanders, C., and Powell, D. A. (2006). Prefrontal control of trace versus delay eyeblink conditioning: Role of the unconditioned stimulus. *Behavioral Neuroscience*, in press.

Oswald, B. B., Maddox, S., and Powell, D. A. (2006). Post-training ibotenic acid lesions to the medial prefrontal cortex interfere with retrieval of the Pavlovian conditioned eyeblink response. *Neurobiology of Learning and Memory*, submitted.

Pavlov, I. (1927). *Conditioned reflexes: An investigation of the physiological activity of the cerebral cortex*. New York, NY: GV Anrep (Trans) Oxford University.

Port, R. L., Romano, A. G., and Patterson, M. M. (1986). Stimulus duration discrimination in the rabbit: Effects of hippocampectomy on discrimination and reversal learning. *Physiological Psychology*, 14, 124-129.

Powell, D. A. (1979). Peripheral and central muscarinic cholinergic blockade: Effects on Pavlovian conditioning. *Bulletin of Psychonomic Society*, 14, 161-164.

Powell, D. A., and Buchanan, S. L. (1980). Autonomic-somatic relationships in the rabbit (oryctolagus cuniculus): Effects of hippocampal lesions. *Physiological Psychology*, 8, 455-462.

Powell, D. A., and Churchwell, J. (2002). Mediodorsal thalamic lesions impair trace eyeblink conditioning in the rabbit. *Learning and Memory*, 9, 10-17.

Powell, D. A., and Ginsberg, J. P. (2005). Single unit activity in the medial prefrontal cortex during Pavlovian heart rate conditioning: Effects of peripheral autonomic blockade. *Neurobiology of Learning and Memory*, 84, 200-213.

Powell, D. A., and Kazis, E. (1976). Blood pressure and heart rate changes accompanying classical eyeblink conditioning in the rabbit (oryctolagus cuniculus). *Psychophysiology*, 13, 441-447.

Powell, D. A., and Levine-Bryce, D. (1988). A comparison of two model systems of associative learning: Heart rate and eyeblink conditioning in the rabbit. *Psychophysiology*, 25, 672-682.

Powell, D. A., and Levine-Bryce, D. (1989). Conditioned bradycardia in the rabbit: Effects of knife cuts and ibotenic acid lesions in the lateral hypothalamus. *Experimental Brain Research*, 76, 103-121.

Powell, D. A., and Lipkin, M. (1975). Heart rate changes accompanying differential classical conditioning of somatic responses in the rabbit. *Bulletin of the Psychonomic Society,* 5, 28-30.

Powell, D. A., Buchanan, S. L., and Gibbs, C. M. (1990). Role of the prefrontal-thalamic axis in classical conditioning. In H. B. M. Uylings, C. G. V. Eden, J. P. C. D. Bruin, M. A. Corner and M. G. P. Feenstra (Eds.), *The prefrontal cortex: Its structure function and pathology progress in brain research* (Vol. 85, pp. 433-466). Amsterdam The Netherlands: Elsevier Science Publishers BV.

Powell, D. A., Churchwell, J., and Burriss, L. (2005). Medial prefrontal lesions and Pavlovian eyeblink and heart rate conditioning: Effects of partial reinforcement on delay and trace conditioning in rabbits (oryctolagus cuniculus). *Behavioral Neuroscience*, 119, 180-189.

Powell, D. A., Gibbs, C. M., Maxwell, B., and Levine-Bryce, D. (1993). On the generality of conditioned bradycardia in rabbits: Assessment of CS and US modality. *Animal Learning and Behavior*, 21, 303-313.

Powell, D. A., Lipkin, M., and Milligan, M. L. (1974). Concomitant changes in classically conditioned heart rate and corneoretinal potential discrimination in the rabbit (oryctolagus cuniculus). *Learning and Motivation*, 5, 532-547.

Powell, D. A., Mankowski, D., and Buchanan, S. L. (1978). Concomitant heart rate and corneoretinal potential conditioning in the rabbit (oryctolagus cuniculus): Effects of caudate lesions. *Physiology and Behavior*, 20, 143-150.

Powell, D. A., Maxwell, B. L., and Penney, J. A. (1996). Neuronal activity in the medial prefrontal cortex during Pavlovian eyeblink and nictitating membrane conditioning. *The Journal of Neuroscience*, 16, 6296-6306.

Powell, D. A., McLaughlin, J., and Chachich, M. (2000). Classical conditioning of autonomic and somatomotor responses and their central nervous system substrates. In J. E. Steinmetz and D. S. Woodruff-Pak (Eds.), *Eyeblink classical conditioning: Volume 2 animal models* (pp. 257-286). Boston, MA: Kluwer Academic Publishers.

Powell, D. A., McLaughlin, J., Churchwell, J., Elgarico, T., and Parker, A. (2002). Heart rate changes accompanying jaw movement Pavlovian conditioning in rabbbits: Concomitant blood pressure adjustments and effects of peripheral autonomic blockade. *Integrative Physiological and Behavioral Science*, 37, 215-227.

Powell, D. A., Skaggs, H., Churchwell, J., and McLaughlin, J. (2001). Post-training lesions of the medial prefrontal cortex impair performance of Pavlovian eyeblink conditioning but have no effect on concomitant heart rate changes. *Behavioral Neuroscience*, 115, 1029-1038.

Powell, D. A., Watson, K., and Maxwell, B. (1994). Involvement of subdivisions of the medial prefrontal cortex in learned cardiac adjustments. *Behavioral Neuroscience,* 108, 294-307.

Prokasy, W. F. (1984). Acquisition of skeletal conditioned responses in Pavlovian conditioning. *Psychophysiology*, 21, 1-13.

Prokasy, W. F., Grant, D. A., and Meyers, N. A. (1958). Eyelid conditioning as a function of unconditioned stimulus intensity and intertrial interval. *Journal of Experimental Psychology*, 55, 242-246.

Quirk, G. J., Armony, J. L., and LeDoux, J. E. (1997). Fear conditioning enhances different temporal components of tone-evoked spike trains in auditory cortex and lateral amygdala. *Neuron*, 19, 613-624.

Quirk, G. J., Russo, G. K., Barron, J. L., and Lebron, K. (2000). The role of ventromedial prefrontal cortex in the recovery of extinguished fear. *The Journal of Neuroscience*, 20, 6225-6231.

Rauch, S. L., and Shin, L. M. (1999). Functional neuroimaging studies in posttraumatic stress disorder. *Annals New York Academy of Sciences*, 821, 83-98.

Reiman, E. M., Lane, R. D., Ahern, G. L., Schwartz, G. E., Davidson, R. J., and Nadel, L. (2000). In: *Positron emission tomography in the study of emotion, anxiety, and anxiety disorders* (pp. 389-406). New York, NY: Oxford University Press.

Robleto, K., Poulos, A. M., and Thompson, R. F. (2004). Brain mechanisms of extinction of the classically conditioned eyeblink response. *Learning and Memory,* 11, 517-524.

Robleto, K., and Thompson, R. F. (2003). Effects of muscimol infusions on the extinction of the classically conditioned nictitating membrane response in the rabbit. *2003 Abstract Viewer/Itinerary Planner*, Program No. 87.6, Online.

Rose, J. E., and Woolsey, C. N. (1948). *The orbitofrontal cortex and its connections with the mediodorsal nucleus in rabbits, sheep and cat.* Association for Research in Nervous and Mental Diseases, 27, 210-232.

Schacter, D. L. (1992). Understanding implicit memory - a cognitive neuroscience approach. *American Psychologist*, 47, 559-569.

Schmajuk, N. A. (1984). Psychological theories of hippocampal function. *Physiological Psychology*, 12, 166-183.

Schneiderman, N. (1972). Response system divergencies in aversive classical conditioning. In A. H. Black and W. F. Prokasy (Eds.), *Classical conditioning ii: Current theory and research* (pp. 341-376). New York NY: Appleton-Centry-Crofts.

Schneiderman, N., and Gormezano, I. (1964). Conditioning of the nictitating membrane of the rabbit as a function of cs-us interval. *Journal of Comparative and Physiological Psychology*, 57, 188-195.

Schwaber, J. S., Kapp, B. S., Higgins, G. A., and Rapp, P. R. (1982). Amygdaloid and basal forebrain direct connections with the nucleus of the solitary tract and the dorsal motor nucleus. *Journal of Neuroscience*, 2, 1424-1438.

Simon, B., Knuckley, B., Churchwell, J., and Powell, D. A. (2005). Post-training lesions of the medial prefrontal cortex interfere with subsequent performance of trace eyeblink conditioning. *The Journal of Neuroscience*, 25, 10740-10746.

Smith, C. N., Clark, R. E., Manns, J. R., and Squire, L. R. (2005). Acquisition of differential delay eyeblink classical conditioning is independent of awareness. *Behavioral Neuroscience*, 119, 78-86.

Smith, O. A., and DeVito, J. L. (1984). Central neural integration for the control of autonomic responses associated with emotion. *Annual Review of Neuroscience,* 7, 43-65.

Solomon, P. R., Stowe, G. T., and Pendlbeury, W. W. (1989). Disrupted eyelid conditioning in a patient with damage to cerebellar afferents. *Behavioral Neuroscience,* 103, 898-902.

Squire, L. R. (1992). Memory and the hippocampus: A synthesis from findings with rats, monkeys, and humans. *Psychological Review*, 99, 195-231.

Squire, L. R., Sporns, O., and Tononi, G. E. (1994). In: *Memory and forgetting: Long-term and gradual changes in memory storage* (pp. 243-269). New York, NY: Academic Press.

Supple, W. F., and Leaton, R. N. (1990). Cerebellar vermis: Essential for classically conditioned bradycardia in the rat. *Brain Research*, 509, 17-23.

Supple, W. F., Jr., and Kapp, B. S. (1993). The anterior cerebellar vermis: Essential involvement in classically conditioned bradycardia in the rabbit. *The Journal of Neuroscience*, 13, 3705-3711.

Takehara, K., Kawahara, S., and Kirino, Y. (2003). Time-dependent reorganization of the brain components underlying memory retention in trace eyeblink conditioning. *The Journal of Neuroscience*, 23, 9897-9905.

Takehara, K., Kawahara, S., Takatsuki, K., and Kirino, Y. (2002). Time-limited role of the hippocampus in the memory for trace eyeblink conditioning in mice. *Brain Research*, 951, 183-190.

Takehara-Nishiuchi, K., Kawahara, S., and Kirino, Y. (2005). NMDA receptor-dependent processes in the medial prefrontal cortex are important for acquisition and the early stage of consolidation during trace, but not delay eyeblink conditioning. *Learning and Memory*, 12, 606-614.

Takehara-Nishiuchi, K., Nakao, K., Kawahara, S., Matsuki, N., and Kirino, Y. (2006). Systems consolidation requires postlearning activation of NMDA receptors in the medial prefrontal cortex in trace eyeblink conditioning. *The Journal of Neuroscience*, 26, 5049-5058

Thomas, G. J., and Gash, D. M. (1988). Differential effects of hippocampal ablations on dispositional and representational memory in the rat. *Behavioral Neuroscience*, 102, 635-642.

Thompson, R. F. (2005). In search of memory traces. *Annual Review of Psychology,* 56, 1-23.

Topka, H., Valls-Sole, J., Massaquoi, S. G., and Hallett, M. (1993). Deficit in classical conditioning in patients with cerebellar degeneration. *Brain*, 116, 961-969.

Tulving, A. (1985). How many memory systems are there? *American Psychologist*, 40, 385.

Vogt, B. A., Sikes, R. W., Swadlow, H. A., and Weyand, T. G. (1986). Rabbit cingulate cortex: Cytoarchitecture, physiological border with visual cortex, and afferent cortical connections of visual, motor, postsubicular, and intracingulate origin. *The Journal of Comparative Neurology*, 248, 74-94.

Vouimba, R. M., Garcia, R., Baudry, M., and Thompson, R. F. (2000). Potentiation of conditioned freezing following dorsomedial prefrontal cortex lesions does not interfere with fear reduction in mice. *Behavioral Neuroscience,* 114, 720-724.

Weible, A. P., McEchron, M. D., and Disterhoft, J. F. (2000). Cortical involvement in acquisition and extinction of trace eyeblink conditioning. *Behavioral Neuroscience*, 114, 1058-1067.

Weinberger, N. M., and Diamond, D. M. (1987). Physiological plasticity in auditory cortex: Rapid induction by learning. *Progress in Neurobiology*, 29, 1-55.

Weiss, C., and Disterhoft, J. F. (1996). Eyeblink conditioning, motor control, and the analysis of limbic-cerebellar interactions. *Behavioral and Brain Sciences*, 19, 479-527.

INDEX

B

C

D

E

H

I

N

Q

R

W

Y

Z